CROSSROADS:
STORIES OF THE RURAL SOUTH

Montress Greene

CROSSROADS: Stories of the Rural South
Copyright © 2022. Montress Greene

Printed in the USA

For information contact
montressgreene@gmail.com
montressgreene.com

979-8-218-09790-5 (paperback)
979-8-218-09791-2 (ebook)

Interior design by Darlene Swanson
www.van-garde.com

Contents

Acknowledgements

CROSSROADS has been a journey and one I would never have reached the destination without a lot of help and encouragement. Ralph Durham and Sharon Durham provided technical support, and cheered me on. They have always been my cheerleaders.

Thanks to Thomas Greene, Betty Bridgers, Fred Bridgers, Richard Greene, Cindy Harris and Janice Greene Proctor for sharing pictures that add so much to this book. They are some awesome pictures and I wish I could use every one of them. Thanks to Fred Bridgers who researched and provided documentation on one of the stories.

Thanks to Stephanie Bass for encouraging me to join the North Carolina Writer's Network, and giving me the nudge I needed early in this process.

The encouragement and positive comments from friends and family are appreciated and I thank you all.

Montress Greene, Author of *CROSSROADS*, 2022

About the Author

MONTRESS GREENE WAS BORN AT Pender's Crossroads, Wilson County, North Carolina. Her stories make you feel like you are there at the country store, on the front porch with family and friends in rocking chairs, with Howard the Goat, on the pond or investigating a murder.

Although this is her first book, Greene became a professional writer in high school by selling book reports to classmates who didn't like to read. Her book reports in the 1950s sold for 50 cents each.

She most fondly remembers her time as a youth on the family farm, exploring the creek, woods, fishpond and other adventures around the Crossroads. She will also share some hardship. Her goal is to entertain you, and invite you to a time long past, but not forgotten.

Bridgers Grocery and Farm Supply 1930's

About Bridgers Store

THE COVER PICTURE IS OF the country store mentioned throughout these stories. The photo was taken about 1938. The young lady
standing in front of the store is Blanche Bridgers, who years later
would operate the store founded in 1922 by her parents, Wright
Bridgers and Martha Sharpe Bridgers. Bridgers Grocery was located
at Pender's Crossroads. After Wright Bridgers passed away in 1941,
the store was operated by Martha Bridgers and daughter, Blanche.

The store was called Blanche Bridgers Grocery, and some called it
"Miss Mothie's." It wasn't just farmers who frequented Bridgers Store.
Many businessmen and local, state and national politicians visited
and swapped stories and all of them wanted the support of Blanche
who was influential during the election seasons. She represented the
farming community and wasn't shy about letting the politicians know
the issues and what it would take to get their votes.

This Country Store was the hub of the rural community, and you
could find neighbors gathered at the store which served the neighborhood not only as a place to buy groceries and farm supplies but as a
kind of Social Club. People stopped in to purchase a few groceries or
to drink a beer and shoot a game of pool and some came by just to
visit with whoever happened to be there.

Some farmers teased each other about driving past other country
stores to come to Bridgers Grocery to get a glimpse of Blanche. I
believe this was true. She was a beautiful woman. She also listened to

them. She had a lot more going for her than just her beauty. She was well known far beyond the crossroads for her passion and commitment to standing up for issues that affected the lives of the farmers and rural folks she loved. Blanche Bridgers may have been a country girl who operated a country store, but she listened to the farmers, and took their concerns to Washington, D.C.

Blanche Bridgers, late 1930's or early 40's,
in front of Bridgers Grocery and Farm Supply

For You, Mama

Dell Bridgers Greene

THIS COLLECTION OF STORIES IS dedicated to my mother, Dell Bridgers Greene. There are a lot of stories in here about my dad and not much about my mother. It is hard to write about someone who was so close to perfection. In her world, there were two ways to do something: It was either right or it was wrong. There was no gray area.

My mama was multi-talented. She loved to sing and dance, and she had a wicked sense of humor. She was a serious thinker and yet she was playful. She skipped two grades and graduated from Gardners High School at the age of fifteen. Her grandchildren could take their algebra or geometry problems to her for help, and she would get them to sit beside her, and she would say, "Let's read the rules first." Then she would proceed to explain the problem to them and get it right. She took French and Latin in high school and 40 years later, she could still pick up a French book and read it. I believe she could have achieved anything. She graduated high school in 1932 when she was just 15 years old, fell in love and married my dad and they had six children. It was my mama who was the disciplinarian and tried to keep us in tow. She sometimes referred to my dad as the "oldest child." She died thirty years before my father.

During seven years of illness, she spent many weeks at Duke Hospital, and she made friends with some of the doctors and corresponded with them for quite some time. Kathryn Graham, owner of the Washington Post, was at Duke where her husband was a patient at the same time my mother was there. Mama and Mrs. Graham became friends and corresponded for years.

If mama were to read these stories, she would most likely pick a few of them and say, "I don't believe I would tell that."

Thank you, mama, for everything. I love you and still miss you. I still sometimes reach for the phone to call and ask your opinion. For You.

Bridger's Grocery and Farm Supply: Country Store at the Crossroads

Wright and Martha Bridgers opened the doors to Bridgers Grocery in the early 1920s. This store was like many other country stores in rural America at the time. It was the meeting place for the neighborhood farmers. Some would bring children who played under the store shelter while the fathers sat on benches and talked. The country store was a place teenagers met, a place where affairs were gossiped and some got their start. It had the big, tall shelter with multi-colored lights all around (after the neighborhood got electricity). The roads were dirt and the ground under the shelter was also dirt, until about 1946 when they were paved. There were several benches under the shelter, and they were usually occupied by men talking about their crops and how much or how little it had rained. They talked about the news, seeds, gardens, fertilizers, gossip, baseball, punch boards and just about everything. The punch board was the rural lottery. There was a big wooden box filled with blocks of ice. There was an ice pick and a pair of ice tongs on a shelf nearby. If you wanted a chunk of ice to take home for iced tea, you could break it off with the pick and lift it with the tongs. It was weighed and I do remember a big chunk of ice was 5-10 cents.

The Author, Montress Greene, age 5.

Another wooden box held fish which were kept iced. There was a drum of kerosene that was pumped out into containers and sold. The gas pump had a glass bowl at the top and a handle to pump gas from the underground tank into the glass bowl. I believe the tank held approximately five gallons. A nozzle was used to empty the gas into a container or into a car gas tank. Before 1942 when the Crossroads got electricity, gravity emptied the bowl.

The store entrance had double screen doors with Merita Bread sign across the front. Just inside the store was the "drink box" and against the wall stood the "ice cream freezer." The ice cream freezer was after 1942 when the Crossroads got electricity. There was a big show case with glass front and around behind the show case was sliding glass doors so my grandmother could retrieve candy, chewing gum, pocket knives, playing cards, rolls for cap pistols, hand lotion, after shave, cigarettes, cigars, chewing tobacco and just about everything one could want at a country store. It was kind of cool when my grandmother would take me behind the "candy counter" and slide

Wright and Martha Bridgers, founders of Bridgers Store.

open the doors and tell me to get some candy. I didn't really like candy so much and sometimes if it was offered, I would tell her I would rather have a wiener or a piece of cheese. Near the back of the store was a large "meat case" which also had a glass front and it displayed, wieners, bologna, hamburger, neck bones, souse, steaks, and various cuts of meat. There was always a round wooden box with cheese which was cut to order. Meats and cheese were weighed and wrapped in thick white butcher paper which hung in a large roll from the ceiling. There was also a bunch of bananas hanging on a piece of hay wire from the ceiling. A customer could pull off one, two, three or however many bananas they wanted right off the bunch.

The second room of the store housed a pool table where the men and boys had a Coca Cola or a beer and talked or gossiped, made bets and laughed at each other's jokes or missed shots on the pool table. There were shelves from the floor to the ceiling all around this room and you could find plow points, nails, plow line (rope), hinges, seed, screws, socks, work shoes, tennis shoes, shirts, overalls, needles, thread, material and so many things I could never remember them all. There was a 55-gallon wooden barrel of molasses that sat on the floor near the pool table. A pump was attached and anyone who wanted molasses brought their jar or container and filled their own or asked Miss Mothie to get it.

Mostly what went on at the store aside from the purchases was a lot of conversation about farming, the War, baseball, hunting, hard core gossip, how hot or cold it was, how much or how little it had rained. There was always laughing and smoking, dipping, spitting and chewing. I honestly believe a country store, or a front porch, is better therapy than a psychiatrist. I just remember it being a fun place. Salesmen were in and out of the store off and on most of the day. They came in and stayed for a while and joined in the conversations. On one of these occasions a man from Green Pond, a section of Wilson or Nash County. I believe he was a Mr. Griffin. The discussion was about dry weather, and each talker had his own story about how many days it had been at their house since it rained, and everybody had a taller tale to add. The man from Green Pond spoke up and said that folks at Penders Crossroads didn't know what dry weather was. He said that Green Pond was the driest place in the world. He went on to add that when Noah built the ark and it rained for forty days and forty nights — Green Pond got only a half inch then. That brought a round of laughter and the conversation shifted to another subject.

The country store was a place for tales and gossip, some true and some not true. The Crossroads was a Peyton Place before it's time.

I still believe the country store and the front porch are, or were, great places for conversations and sharing the good and bad of daily life around the Crossroads.

I do remember when I first started working at BB&T in 1954 and lived with my uncle about 15 blocks from the bank near Atlantic Christian College, I walked to and from work every day. When I walked home in the afternoon, most houses had a front porch and people were sitting on the porch and children were playing in the yard. I met many of these folks and enjoyed joining the conversation for a few minutes on my walk home. I would just stop and greet the porch sitters with "Hey, how are you folks? Beautiful day for the kids to play outside." If I had not met them before I would introduce myself and the conversation would be one that is typical of Wilson County and most rural areas. It was about who my folks were and many times a connection could be made that they knew some of my family or I knew theirs. Many of these people were familiar with

Bridgers Grocery and had stopped there. It was a down home comforting feeling and one that is mostly missing today.

People are not sitting on the porches today and country stores are mostly closed. They are around in the back of their houses. I am glad I was around to enjoy a front porch and a country store. Most houses today do not have, or do not use, the front porch. People have added patios in the back of the house, and they are great places to relax or entertain but they are not as inviting as a "front porch" with rocking chairs and porch swings occupied by family and friends and all of them loved to talk.

No one needed an invitation to join a group of family and friends on the porch. Anyone passing by who chose would just stop and join in the conversation and were welcomed. A neighbor would stop by and talk for a while and leave only to have another take his or her place on the porch.

Country stores and front porches were therapy.

Alvis Greene Grocery: Country Store at the Crossroads

THERE WAS A SECOND STORE at Penders Crossroads, Alvis Greene Grocery, and it was another place for farmers to gather, shop and socialize. The two stores were across the road from each other. This store building was smaller but the folks meeting there were just as lively and interesting. In fact, they were mostly the same folks. You would think two country stores close enough together to throw a rock and hit the other would be like dueling banjos and have a competitive dislike but that was not the case. It was a friendly atmosphere, and it was family. Alvis was my father's brother, and he was one of the friendliest and most entertaining people I ever knew. He was also a big teaser.

Alvis and Mildred Greene owned the store, and you could always find one or both of them there. This store had been operated in the1930s and early 1940s by Lee and Nolia Petway. The Petways moved away from the Crossroads sometime in the early 1940s. My uncle, Alvis Greene, opened the store in the late 1950s.

Alvis's store was big on personality and fun. It, too, had a pool table and a pot belly stove and some of the same conversations could be enjoyed there. The farmers and others came and sat on the wooden Pepsi and Coca Cola crates, rocked back and forth and told their stories about crops, baseball, how much or how little rain, seed, fertilizers, auto racing and, of course, a little neighborhood gossip.

Alvis and Mildred Greene in Newport News during WWll

Uncle Alvis was an avid baseball fan and during baseball season, his radio was broadcasting the play by play of every game and Alvis could tell you all the stats. He enjoyed the sport and usually had folks in the store to listen to the games with him and he loved the interaction. The auto races were another favorite topic of conversation. There were discussions about whether a Ford, Chevrolet or a Dodge was faster and which drivers were the best. Another pastime at Alvis's store was some friendly card games. I believe the game of choice was Hearts and maybe some other games. There was a pool table in the store and the men and boys were likely to be playing a game of pool, laughing at each other's jokes and missed shots.

Aunt Mildred could either be found running the store, while Uncle Alvis was farming, or she would be at the house next to the store. I loved going to her house and visiting with her. She was so kind to me, and she always engaged in conversation, even when I was a child. Some adults didn't include children in conversations, but Aunt Mildred always made me feel special. She had a great personality and had a hearty sincere laugh. I remember her as a warm and loving person. Another reason I loved going to her house was that she was an excellent cook and always had some homemade goodies. She was a special lady.

Two country stores gave the Crossroads the feeling of a small village. Yes, it was a village with special folks living up and down the five roads that led to the Crossroads.

Janice, Martha and Montress Greene, early 1940's.

The 1940s: Investigations and Adventures

My cousin Janice and I were about nine years old and in our search for an adventure, so we made our way to the fishpond. No one knew where we were. We would tell my mama we were going to our grandmother's and tell our grandmother we were going to my house. We would not have been given permission to go to the pond and untie the row boat. The pond water was not clear like the creek. It was dark and murky and what was underneath was a mystery, one we were determined to solve. We must have had an overactive imagination. We paddled across the pond and talked about what mysterious things lay underneath the murky water. The only activity was an occasional fish breaking the surface or a turtle swimming nearby.

Sometimes Mag would be on her stool fishing, and she just told us to row that boat on by and stay far away from her and not scare the fish away. Most of the time nobody was around.

We searched for clues to some imaginary crime. In the middle of the pond was a group of four or five trees. We rowed the boat to the shade underneath those trees and examined the sticks, leaves, a cork, or whatever we could reach from the boat.

We would pretend the trees were palms on some tropical island and we were there to investigate some criminal activity. On this day somehow Janice was standing in the boat or leaning over the side to grab some evidence. I don't remember how but she fell out of the boat into the water. She was struggling to get back in the boat but kept falling back. The small row boat was rocking. We were both afraid the boat would turn over. Neither of us could swim well enough to manage a capsized vessel. I would get on the opposite side from her to try to keep the boat upright. Nothing seemed to work. It took a while for her to get back into the boat, but I don't remember exactly how she got in. Janice and I talked about this day recently and she said that I pulled her back into the boat. I don't remember, but I am happy I did. She is now 87 years old, and we talk almost every day.

This one was not imaginary. A murder investigation was one of our adventures. I don't know where the murder took place, but there was a victim's body, thrown or taken from a taxi, found early one morning in the ditch just a short distance behind my grandmother's store. Another grandmother lived on the dirt road behind the store, and the body was found even closer to her house. The Sheriff's Department gathered evidence and filed their report. They took down the crime-scene tape and left the scene. At the store, there was much speculation about the murder. Folks talked about who was driving the taxi, the victim, and who else was in the taxi.

The Sheriff's Department finished, so Janice and I took over the investigation and made our way to the ditch where the body was dumped. We gathered evidence. Cigarette butts, footprints, tire tracks, chewing gum wrapper, broken twigs, etc. We sat on the clay bank and tried to recreate the crime, talk about our evidence and solve the case. Of course, we were there without permission.

Neither of us played with baby dolls or girlie things. We had way too many adventures in the woods, fields, ponds or ditches. The crime was not solved by us, but we sure did play detective for a few days.

In 1946 (I believe that is the year) the road between Wilbanks and Town Creek was paved. That road went in front of my grandmother's store. We found a new adventure on the newly paved road. Janice had a pair of the old metal roller skates, the ones you put on over shoes and tighten to fit. There was a bicycle and rope at my house. We had a plan. The road between the crossroads and Hwy. 42 was called "roller coaster road" because of the hills.

We tied the rope to the bicycle seat. We took turns — one of us rode the bicycle and the other one wore the skates and held onto the rope. It was like skiing on skates. Going up the hill was sorta slow but coming down the other side was fast. Sometimes the one on skates caught up to the bicycle and we were all over the newly paved road. Automobile traffic was almost nonexistent — a car once on a while. One of those hills went right past Mr. Ransome Benton's house. Mr. Ransome was a friend of my dad and a regular at the store. He saw us and went to the store and told my father what we were doing. At that time my father had a black panel truck. He drove up beside us, took the bicycle and rope and the skates, put them in the truck and took Janice to my grandmother's and took me home. He didn't say a word to us.

When he put me out at our house all he said was "Don't do that again. Someone driving a car might not see you."

We knew some of the neighborhood men, including her father and mine, who were brothers played poker in a wooded area behind the store. We would go to their "spot" when it was vacant. There was a nail barrel turned upside down for a card table, Pepsi or Coca Cola crates or a stump for chairs. We would find candy wrappers, beer bottles, soft drink bottles, cigarette or cigar butts. We would sit at the crudely made poker table and talk. In our minds it was like a bar in the western movies of the time. I don't remember playing cards.

I did get into trouble for one of our investigations. There was a suicide in the wooded area behind the store. Of course, when we heard about it, we felt the need to investigate. We did and without going into detail, I will just say we once again looked for and collected evidence like in the Roy Rogers movies. My mother was not pleased about it. I don't remember about Janice, but I got my butt burned because of that one.

If you don't know what tobacco "plant beds" were like this one may not make sense. A big garden like area is marked off and tilled. Tobacco seeds are sewn all over the bed. When the plants start coming up, they are fragile. In order to protect the plants, the farmer bends reeds like a bow and sticks both ends of the reed into the ground. These bows are placed all over the plant bed a few feet apart and then a large cheese cloth is stretched all over the reeds and the reeds hold the cover about 10 or 12 inches off the fragile plants. It is kind of like a trampoline but, of course, not strong enough to do what we did. We decided to run across the plant bed and bounce on that cover. The cover protected the plants from most animals that may walk on them, and most animals did not walk on the bouncy cover. We were not most animals. We ran back and forth kind of bouncing and every step we took came down on those precious tobacco plants.

The owner of the plant bed discovered the damage — and we were caught. The plants were damaged, and I remember my dad trying to help salvage some plants and also sharing tobacco plants when it was time to set the plants in the tobacco fields. That was not one of our finest days. The bed belonged to Mr. Fred Mangum. I got a lecture for this one. I am friends and FB friends with Mr. Fred's daughter, Page, now. If she reads this, I hope we remain friends.

Rural Health Care in the 1940s

EDGECOMBE COUNTY. 1940s & 50s Rural Health Care up close: I am going to share a memory of what basic health care and disease prevention looked like to me as a child in the 1940s. Here goes: My Aunt Minnie was an RN and worked as a Public Health Nurse in Edgecombe County, NC. When I was between the ages of seven and twelve years old, I visited with her for several days at a time over those years and travelled with her throughout rural Edgecombe County to see residents and attend to the most basic health care of those mostly rural folks. We started out early in the morning in her green Plymouth which I thought was one of the prettiest cars I ever saw.

Minnie Greene, RN.

Aunt Minnie loaded the Plymouth back seat with bandages, first-aid items, vitamins, a box of papers, and a couple of white enamel trays containing needles, syringes and vials of medicines. I remember some being immunizations, because she jabbed us with those needles on occasion.

19

We crossed creeks on loose-board bridges that rumbled, which was rather scary. After a heavy rain, there was always that threat of getting stuck or sliding into a ditch on a clay hill. These roads wound through wooded areas. The houses were mostly dilapidated and occupied by both black and white families. All were treated and greeted the same. Aunt Minnie stopped at each and every house. We would get out of the car, and she greeted whoever was in the yard or on the porch with a smile and positive comments. If there was no one outside, she knocked on the door and called out the resident by name. Yes, she knew them all.

It was like a social call because she engaged the woman or mother or grandmother in a conversation which helped her to get a general picture of "how everyone in the house was doing." Once she got that information, she called each child to her by name and talked with the child while looking in the child's ears, putting that wooden stick or tongue depressor in their mouth to look at the throat. I remember her asking children to walk across the room while she watched. Note here: (She must have done that for me because she took me to Webb's Wilson Shoe Store, and I was fitted with "Proper Built Shoes" to correct something about my feet. They were brown brogan like shoes and were as ugly as sin, but I wore them for several years. Some pictures of me during that time show those ugly butt shoes).

If a child or adult had a minor injury, she bandaged it and told them how to care for it to prevent infection. Aunt Minnie even had an eye chart and asked the children to identify the animals or shapes on the chart. If there were problems that needed attention, she made a record and asked that they come into the Health Department in Tarboro to see the Public Health doctor. Most of these folks were either sharecroppers or farm laborers who worked by the day in the fields. Most had no transportation, so she helped arrange for them to get to the Health Department. Children's general health, weight and other information was documented on that child's chart. When she went back to that house in a month or so, she had a record. No, there were no computers, but her information was pretty darned complete and not code words but solid information.

I remember conversations about diet and how to use what they had access to in a healthy way. Aunt Minnie even encountered a few cases where domestic violence was evident. I remember her calling the husband out of the field and having a conversation that lasted for quite a while. I think this was an effort on her part to counsel this family on issues of a personal nature because it also had to do with the health of the family.

When her examinations and conversations were finished at one dilapidated house she loaded up on the green Plymouth and went to the next house. Let me say that the physical condition of the houses was dilapidated but the people who lived in those houses were not. They were strong, hardworking, determined good hearted, intelligent people who were striving to take care of themselves and their families against the odds of extreme poverty. Yes, their health and safety were at risk. Farm labor was intense and dangerous especially for the children who were part of the labor force. This poverty did not interfere with their happy attitudes and ability to connect with the "Health Nurse" and even that girl with pigtails wearing those ugly brown shoes.

Looking back this was basic health care at its best and a most efficient way of providing it. As we drove away from the house, we could see the whole family waving good-bye. I do remember going into some of the homes and we were invited to have a glass of iced tea and a piece of pie or cake. On other occasions we would "stay and take dinner" with the family. I remember fried chicken, collards, corn bread and fried fat back. Aunt Minnie did not eat from fast food restaurants (there were not any at the time). She ate with the people she served and cared for, and she was welcomed. As we drove to the next house, she would tell me who lived at the house we were headed.

Minnie, Janice, Montress Greene and Dell Bridgers Greene.

On one stop we encountered an elderly black woman who had her sewing machine set up in her "front room" and was making suits, coats and other beautiful pieces of clothing. I remember watching and saying that I wanted a coat like one she was making. She told me she would make one for me. She called me to her and measured me from top to tip of my fingers. A month or so later I went with Aunt Minnie to that same house and had a big surprise. The lady seamstress had not forgotten me. She had made a beautiful brown wool coat with a felt collar and a beautiful tan satin lining. I feel sure Aunt Minnie provided the material and paid her.

In the afternoon we rode the green Plymouth back to Tarboro and went to the Court House where the Edgecombe County Health Dept. was located and occupied one fairly large room and a few desks and a private office for the Public Health Doctor. This process went on every day by my aunt and several other RNs who traveled other country roads. Somehow, I think the basic health care these folks got was pretty darned good. I still remember some of the people I met on those days in Edgecombe County traveling those dirt roads in that green Plymouth.

Axel

IT WAS A COOL FALL day in 1939 and the colors of leaves and grasses along the dirt roadside were vibrant yellows, orange and brown. Axel had slept last night inside a storage building behind a small country Baptist church. He noticed the hinges on the shed door were sagging. He found some tools and nails in the shed and repaired the sagging door. In his mind the repair job would be his way of saying thanks for shelter. They may notice the door is repaired or they may not. Early this morning he closed the shed door, which now closed easily and securely and he left.

He walked alone when he left Northern Virginia until he crossed into the State of North Carolina. About two miles inside N.C. he noticed a large brown dog following a safe distance behind him. The dog would jump the ditch and go into the woods, and reappear down the road a bit. He and the brown dog kept an eye on each other as they walked.

Axel had started this journey on foot two months ago. He was a broken man in so many ways. Life had been good for Axel after he married Lilly Anne. He worked several jobs in his youth but found his career as a carpenter. Lily Anne worked at a doctor's office in Manassas. They located a small house, purchased it and made it their home. Axel used his carpentry skills to make improvements and Lily Anne used her decorating talent to make it a home.

Their life was close to the American dream at that time. They had lived through and survived the Great Depression but even that didn't prepare them for the hardships ahead. In June of 1937 Lily Ann became sick. There were doctor bills, treatments and hospital bills. The loss of her income plus the added medical bills put the two in a financial bind. In February of 1938 Lily Anne died. It was not only the biggest personal loss of Axel's life, he also lost the house they had worked so hard for and called home. After Lily Anne's death, nothing seemed to go right for Axel. He is now 60 years old and was diagnosed with depression and arthritis. He lost his carpentry job.

He knew he had family in a small town in North Carolina so he started out on foot toward Sharpsburg, NC. He felt that his life would get better if he could reach his family. He could not call them because they didn't have phones, and he didn't want to ask for help until he could look them in the eye. He made a decision to just show up and maybe they could help each other. He did second-guess his decision now and then but continued walking toward Sharpsburg.

Persevering through rain and cold, or gratefully appreciating the crisp fall air, depending on the day, he continued to walk south. The large brown dog came closer and closer to Axel. He called the dog Big Boy and he spoke to him about his plight. It took a few days for the Big Boy and Axel to trust each other. Sometimes he felt the dog understood. Axel stopped along the way at farmhouses and country stores and asked for work. Sometimes he would sleep in a shed with the dog for a week or more if work was available. Some storekeepers would trade food and supplies for his labor. The brown dog was now a companion and food for Big Boy was part of his pay. On the cold fall nights, the dog slept close to Axel and the warmth was welcome.

Axel and Big Boy became close and watched out for each other.

One afternoon as the walked along a country road near Scotland Neck a car stopped in the road and the two occupants who were teenagers yelled at him and told him to "beat it." Axel nodded at them and told them he was leaving. The two got out of the car and walked toward Axel. The two made threats and Axel knew he was too old and too sick to defend himself. The two came closer and Axel braced himself for what he felt was coming. When the two teens got within a couple of feet of Axel, the large brown dog came bounding out of the ditch and placed himself between Axel and the would-be attackers. Big Boy growled, barked and showed his teeth. The two teens ran back to their car with the brown dog on their heels. After the car was out of sight Axel sat on the ditch bank holding onto the dog and he felt tears on his face. This big dog was now his friend and protector.

When Axel got a few miles from Tarboro he stopped at a country store. He asked the storekeeper if he needed some work done. The storekeeper told him he did not but that some of the farmers may need some help. Axel and the storekeeper talked until some of the local peanut farmers came in for their daily Pepsi break. One of the farmers offered him a job "shaking peanuts." He accepted the offer although he had never done it before. Axel rode to the peanut field on the back of a mule drawn wagon with the brown dog following. The farmer said the dog could stay as long as he didn't bother the other workers.

Shaking peanuts turned out to be a back bending and dirty job but Axel was grateful to have it. The fields covered acres and acres. The peanuts grew in the ground underneath the plant. Each plant or vine was pulled up by hand and the dirt had to be shaken out of the peanuts. The peanuts and vines were then stacked around a pole like a haystack. It looked like a teepee. Axel worked at this for a week until the peanuts were all pulled up and neatly stacked. The brown dog went to the field every day and watched. Axel and the dog were well fed by the farmer. He even had a few dollars in his pocket.

When the weekend came, Axel and Big Boy started walking toward Sharpsburg again.

On Saturday afternoon it started raining and the wind was twisting the tops of the tall pine trees. They came up to a barn near the roadside but no house was near it. Axel and the dog got inside the old barn. It was dry and they were safe from the storm. He could hear the thunder, wind howling and the heavy rain pouring on the rusty tin roof. Both he and the brown dog were grateful for the shelter. They slept peacefully and woke up rested and ready to continue the journey to find his family. Axel had food in a paper bag. He and the dog shared. They had rainwater to drink.

It was a sunny and crisp day after the stormy night. His grandfather had told him that storms brought a new energy in the atmosphere. He smiled as he walked and thought about this and other things his grandfather told him. It certainly seemed that the air had renewed energy.

He stopped at a creek and rigged a line hoping to catch a fish or two. He didn't have to dig but a few inches in the moist creek bank to find bait. The dog watched him patiently while he waited for a fish to bite. After losing his bait a few times, he finally caught a fish. Axel cleaned the fish and made a small fire. He made a spit and secured the fish over the heat, The brown dog's tail wagged with excitement. Man and dog shared the fish dinner and both were proud of the catch.

Axel knew he was getting close to Sharpsburg and was feeling excited and a little apprehensive. He was both excited and a little hesitant about seeing his cousin Robert. The two had been close as children and had seen each other as adults only a few times. He kept walking toward Sharpsburg with the big brown dog.

He walked on and that afternoon he saw a store. He stopped and there were a few men under the store shelter. He and the dog approached and they were greeted with friendly comments. They were interested in who he was and where he came from. Axel shared some of his story and the more he talked about his journey and his life, the more these men wanted to know. They seemed to be genuinely interested. Some of his story was emotional but he shared the details. He told them about having a cousin in Sharpsburg and his hope that it would turn out to be a good move.

One of the men told Axel that Sharpsburg was only about 10 miles away and that he would give him a ride. Axel replied that he had the dog and how important the dog had been on his journey and he would never leave him. It was agreed that the dog could ride in the truck too.

Axel was feeling much better after talking with these people. He had flashbacks to the attempted attack by those two teenagers. The kindness of the men at this country store restored his faith in strangers. The ride to Sharpsburg was so amazingly short. Axel had been offered some rides along the way and he accepted a few. He felt these folks genuinely wanted to help him. They arrived in Sharpsburg and Axel explained he didn't know exactly where his cousin lived and asked the man to just drop him off at the small cafe and give him some time to inquire about his cousin.

He and the dog exited the truck and thanked the driver. The truck and driver left Axel and his dog in front of the cafe. Axel and the dog sat on a bench getting a feel for this place where he hoped to find his cousin and peace.

The owner of the cafe watched Axel and the dog for a few minutes and he saw the bond between the two. He went outside and said to Axel, "Good afternoon, Sir, you look like you could use a cup of coffee. I just made a fresh pot. Come on in and bring that dog".

Horse and Buggy Joy Ride

SINCE THERE WERE NO TELEVISIONS, telephones and video games we found our own entertainment and sometimes we could get into a bit of trouble. My cousin Janice and I were adventurous and always looking for the next hill. There were five roads that met at my grandmother's store, and we knew all the folks for miles, so we felt safe. We could be a little conniving. Occasionally if we knew we would be told "no" we would tell my mother we were going to her house and tell my grandmothers we were going to my house, and we would take off to the fish pond or some other adventure.

We did not plan things sometimes. They just seemed to happen. I remember well one of those days. My uncle had a horse and buggy. His horse was not just a horse. This was a "horse," a big horse like the Budweiser horses. Although the horse was huge, he was gentle and sweet, and we went by to say hello to the horse and then it happened. We decided, without asking anyone, to hitch this beautiful huge horse to the buggy and go for a ride. We were about 10 years old. So, we did. Two young girls on a buggy took off and rode with no knowledge of the limits for the horse. Looking back, I cannot figure how we got the horse geared up and hitched to the buggy. We certainly had no experience, and I cannot believe the horse cooperated enough for us to get it done. But we did it. We were characters in a Roy Rogers/Dale Evans movie for that afternoon. I have no idea how many miles we rode but it was for hours.

Almost all the side roads were still dirt roads and we rarely saw a car. We played our parts pretty well that day and we did have a lot of fun.

Late in the afternoon we saw the sign indicating Wilson/Edgecombe County line and decided we had gone far enough. Children go to the county fair and pay a dime to ride a pony in a circle about three or four times. We had done that and loved it, but on this day we had the horse and buggy all day and felt free. It was getting dark, so we decided it was time to go back home. The horse took us home, and we had no idea how much trouble we were in.

When we came in my grandmother's yard, she was waiting for us. She was furious. She fussed at us the whole time she was helping get the horse unhitched. She put a blanket over that big horse and told us to take the reins and to walk him until he cooled off and we were not to stop if it took all night. I remember her saying "If this horse dies, I am going to whip you both." That is when I knew we had made a big mistake that day. She may have given spankings to grandchildren, but I had never heard her even threaten; so, I knew we were in big trouble. That is the only time I ever heard her even mention a spanking, not that we didn't need one occasionally. It turned out that the horse was just fine, but we didn't do that ride again.

At about that age, "town children" were probably going to the pool, camps, dancing lessons, learning to play bridge or canasta or going to a movie. They had wonderful experiences that we did not have, but then we were kind of "free range children."

Take a Ride on a Bumpy Road

I WAS JUST THINKING ABOUT a short road trip right here in Wilson County. On this outing I was showing my children a couple of roads less traveled like my father showed me. There was one road in particular that was few miles from my dad's home. Of course, when I rode with him, there was always a story for every field, pond or woods. There was a side road that had been a dirt road when my dad told me to make that turn off of NC 42 East and he would show me where he went quail hunting for many years. His stories detailed the pointing and retrieving skills of an English Setter named "Jake." Jake was one of his first and favorite English Setters about 70 years before our local road trip. My father lived to be 101 and even when he was physically unable to take his dogs quail hunting he kept an English Setter until the end of his life.

Anyway, he talked about things like "Mr. So and So came home from the Civil War and built a house right on that hill…." The story would go on about the wife and children and who she married when her Civil War Vet husband died and the crops they grew.

I remember he said to me "I quail hunted in this area and Jake and I always found a covey or two."

I said to him that it was a pretty long way from his house. He said "No, it wasn't far — just a few miles — but I did get hungry sometimes when I started walking home but during quail season there was always a soy bean field and I would pull off some soy beans and they were a pretty good snack until I got home".

The road we were on is a little different now. It is still narrow, and it actually covers about 4 or 5 miles — part of this road is in Wilson County and part in Edgecombe County. When I took that road recently just because it was there and because of memories with my dad, there were some changes. The road was still curvy, BUT the Wilson County part has been paved — still narrow but paved. When you get to the Edgecombe County line the pavement stops and it becomes a dirt path/road like it was many years ago.

My thoughts were about how we "pave" so much. Yeah, I am old enough to remember many roads that were dirt and I enjoy driving on paved smooth roads as much as anyone.

I have to say that driving on some Interstate or roads that by-pass most of the really interesting things like seeing the virgin woods, creeks up close with a turtle sunning, buzzards, hawks, and the quietness of those remote places, old barns, outhouse Lillie's on the ditch banks, and there are no other cars — or rarely.

Not trying to rail against progress but just happy that I have some of these memories of a simpler time.

The Edgecombe County part of that road is dirt and a bumpier ride. Those bumps make us slow down and see the sights nature provides up close.

Just a memory. Make some memories and take a ride on a bumpy dirt road.

Water Flows from West to East

THIS IS NOT FROM ANY scientific study, and I feel sure that the direction water flows varies depending on where you are.

Most towns and neighborhoods in our area of North Carolina have the large expensive homes on the west side of town and the smaller less expensive homes on the east side.

My information is that this all started years ago before we had the modern sewer systems and water treatment plants. Since there was no sewer system the runoff from outhouses and other waste materials (later years this included chemicals) flowed to the East. That meant the dirty and contaminated sewage and waste from the businesses, factories and residents on the West side flowed on to the East side of town where the poorer people lived.

In my hometown it certainly is true. The Country Club and big homes are right there on the West Side and the small homes, factories and railroad tracks are on the East side.

This was remedied only because of modern sewage systems and sophisticated water treatment plants. Now the citizens on the East side drink clean water from the same system as those on the West Side. That is one step in the right direction. We still have a long way to go.

Running a Straight Row

It was a spring day in 1941 and if Tony had not been 'running tobacco rows' in a field near the creek, it would have been a day with no special memories.

I had been at my Granny Nannie and Grandpa's that day and we fed chickens, checked on the livestock and helped my grandmother build a biddy pen with tobacco sticks, gathered eggs and moved little chicks from the hatching nest to the stick pen and went with Granny to ring the big loud dinner bell so the farm workers would know the time. Not many folks wore a watch at that time. We children ran through the wheat fields with growth almost as tall as we were, played with the hounds, sat quietly with my grandmother after dinner (now lunch) and listened to 'The Lone Ranger' on the big battery radio.

Sometime in the afternoon Grandpa said he was going to some of the fields to see the fields being plowed for tobacco. There were paths around all his fields so he could drive around them and see the progress of planting season. Grandpa told my brother and me that we could ride with him to the fields, so we loaded up in his big red Hudson. He drove on the paths most of the time, but he was known to take that car across the field if he struck the notion. We stopped and he talked with the different tenants, and he seemed to be pleased with their progress. My Grandpa was about 6 ft. 4 in. tall and had a powerful voice and presence. He could be intimidating at times, but he was actually a gentle giant.

Although tobacco was the big Wilson County 'money crop', my grandpa loved growing wheat. He liked looking at the big fields and there was not a lot of hard work in growing and harvesting the wheat like the intense care and work of the tobacco crop. He always had some wheat fields he could see from his front porch. It was like a sea of grass.

On that day in the spring of 1941, the tenants were preparing to pick the fragile tobacco plants from the plant beds and transplant them in the large tobacco fields. The first step was to 'run the rows' and it was important to run them straight, so they were easier to plow, chop and harvest.

All was going well until we got to one of the backfields where Tony was running rows with a mule and a plow. This was before tractors. We drove right up to the end of the row and waited until Tony and the mule got to where he had stopped the big red Hudson. He was upset that the rows were not straight. He used a few cuss words and was upset with Tony. He grumbled about how anybody could 'follow a crooked row.' When Tony got the end of the row where we were, Grandpa cussed a little at Tony about the crooked row and watched while he ran another one. Grandpa told him to try another one. Tony did and it was still not straight. By this time Grandpa is frustrated. Tony was trying.

After several attempts at running the straight row, Grandpa said to Tony "I am going back to the house and get my gun and if you don't run a straight row, I am going to shoot you." We loaded up in the Hudson and drove back to the house where he did get his gun. I remember wondering what was going to happen. We returned to the field and Grandpa got his gun and stood at the end of the row and gave Tony another warning. Tony clucked at the mule and ran yet another row and when he got back to where we were, Grandpa used a few more cuss words and I was afraid he was going to shoot Tony. He didn't and I don't believe he had any intention of doing so. What he did was to say, "Here, YOU take the gun, give me the plow and if I can't run a row straighter that this, then I want you to shoot me."

First Cotton Blossom

ROBERT EARL AND MR. HARVEY both lived near the Crossroads and grew tobacco, corn, cotton and vegetable gardens. These two gentlemen grew up in the neighborhood, inherited their family farms and have remained on the land their forefathers left for them. The two farms joined so the two men interacted on a daily basis just as they had as children and as their families had for decades. Mr. Harvey's parents passed away in 1934 and Robert Earl's parents passed away about a year later. They were young men when each of them started their own careers as farmers. They came of age during the Great Depression and saw up close the hardships of people. They had learned survival skills from parents and grandparents that would serve them well.

The two young men had grown up around the country store and spent hours each week with their fathers who sat on wood crates or a warehouse bench talking with other farmers. The conversations were not just about farming. They learned about life, crops, baseball, politics, and the strengths and weaknesses of people. They learned the importance of friendships and how to vent at the store rather than at home. They found that most folks had some kind of problems and they shared the issues, took to heart most of the reactions as good-natured solutions. They learned to listen to their neighbors and to their elders.

Robert Earl and Harvey were competitive as young boys and had some intense games of shooting marbles. They compared their marbles and each boy explained the merits of his favorite glass balls. They were especially proud of the "steels" and the "log carts". These two young boys would draw a circle in the dirt and take out their best marbles in preparation for the match. They got on their knees in the dirt around the circle. The game would go on until one or the other finally gave in and went home with fewer marbles than he started with. Both boys would have at least one new hole in their overalls. The loser would go to the country store at the Crossroads and trade a few of his father's hen eggs for a little brown bag of new marbles. He would open the bag and examine each glass marble, feel it and decide which were best. The winner would go home and count his winnings and check out his newly won marbles, examining each one and picking his best for the next game.

The competition was ongoing. As teenagers they started to notice the young teenage girls at school, church and around the neighborhood. Most of their interaction with girls was at school and church. It was the 1930's so meeting girls was mostly at festive events, parades, school activities and church socials. Farm work also sometimes brought boys and girls together, with work like tobacco tying. But maybe the most unique meeting venue for boys and girls to get together was the neighborhood dances held in pack houses. After the tobacco was all graded and taken to the market and the pack houses were empty, some farmers cleaned the floors, washed the windows and decorated the barn or pack house getting ready for the dances. The music was provided by locals who played guitar, drums, fiddle or whatever instrument they had. Young girls dressed in their best party dresses and spent most of the day primping and getting the ribbons in their hair just right. Young men and boys made sure their hair was clean and combed and that they were dressed and even felt dapper. The competition between Robert Earl and Harvey continued as each competed for the affections of the prettiest girls. It was the same competitive spirit as those games of marbles. Each of these guys was always trying to outdo the other.

In the early 1940's the War was talked about at the crossroads store every day and people shared news from family members and sometimes read the letters from soldiers. It was an emotional time when these letters were read aloud. The wood crates stopped rocking back and forth. Everyone sat perfectly still and listened for first hand news from the battle ships and from the battlefield. A soldier wrote about how one of his buddies had died from enemy fire and others suffered serious wounds. He told about how they dug foxholes and had to abandon them because of grenades. They wrote about heroic actions taken by buddies. Sometimes the letters included pictures that were passed around. Some pictures taken on the battlefield were unsettling and it wasn't unusual for some of those grown men to shed a few tears. There were some pictures of the soldiers horsing around laughing. The soldiers in these pictures had left the crossroads and other parts of the country as eighteen year old boys. These pictures showed they had become men and soldiers who were fighting for their country.

The effects of the War had reached every neighborhood in the country in some way. There were shortages of many items and rations had been put in place to prevent hoarding and black market practices. Gasoline, sugar, milk, shoes and most items were rationed. If a person needed shoes for his family, he had to have a stamp authorizing him to make the purchase. The stamp gave him permission to purchase and gave the merchants permission to make the sale. The stamps had no monetary value. Much of the workforce had gone into the military or had been drafted to serve. Women who had dreamed of being a homemaker and had no interest in working in factories or driving trucks and tractors found it necessary to do those jobs vacated by the men who are now soldiers. Women rose to the occasion and became important to the workforce in the country. Although these changes were taking place, life went on with as much normalcy as was possible.

Robert Earl had fallen for a neighborhood girl named Becky Lynn and Harvey was keeping serious company with Mattie, a girl he had gone to school with. There wasn't any competition here. Both Robert Earl and Harvey had found the girl they wanted as a life partner.

Harvey and Mattie got married in the small Baptist Church. It was a simple ceremony and the honeymoon was a weekend trip to Carolina Beach.

Robert Earl and Becky Lynn got married by the Justice of the Peace, and their honeymoon was a few days in the North Carolina Mountains.

In 1940 Robert Earl was drafted into the United States Army and left the farm he had inherited and left his young wife behind while he served his country. World War Two was a big topic at the Crossroads store and Robert Earl was one of several young men who had been drafted. Harvey had not received a draft notice but he went into town to the Air Force Recruiter and joined the United States Air Force to serve his country, leaving his young wife to operate the farm. Neighbors stepped in and helped. The two young men were away from the farms and from the Crossroads most of the next four years. When they came home on leave they did what they could in a short time on the farms but left most of the responsibility to their families and their neighbors, who willingly helped. There were shortages of clothing, food and most goods during the War. Rural folks and farmers worked hard and they were able to grow most of their food so life continued to have some normalcy.

Life around the Crossroads went on. Tobacco, cotton, corn, wheat, vegetables, fruit trees were grown. The crops were harvested and sold. The fruits and vegetables were harvested and preserved. Livestock, chickens and turkeys were raised for food. There were very few freezers at that time so the vegetables were canned and the fruit was canned, dried or made into jellies or preserves. Most farmers had and shared food. Family and friends who lived in town came out to the farms and picked beans, peas, berries, fruits and vegetables to help with their food needs. There were no severe food shortages like in some large cities. There was help for the elderly, disabled and poorest folks in the neighborhood. The Crossroads was a small village and folks watched out for each other.

Robert Earl and Harvey returned from their duties in the U.S. Military in 1945. They changed from the Military Uniforms back into their overalls and work kakis. They had both served their country and the War was over. Hitler was no longer a threat and the pride in country and positive attitude for the future ran high.

Harvey and Robert Earl returned to the tobacco and cotton fields. They worked hard and took advantage of some of the GI benefits for education and loans. The two met neighbors at the country store and swapped stories with whoever happened to be present. Their wives became friends and were aware of the competition between the two men. It was a friendly competition about who had the first barn of tobacco ready for market or who made the most pounds per acre or who caught the biggest fish on a fishing trip. It was good natured and made great conversation and a lot of laughing at themselves and each other. It seemed that Harvey somehow came out on top of so many of the competitive events.

One big title to be won each spring was awarded to the farmer who had the first cotton blossom. Farmers watched their cotton fields closely and were out early every morning to check for that first cotton blossom. The farmer who had the first blossom would quickly take it to Elm City and show it off at the Hardware Store, Drug Store and Barber Shop. The cotton blossom was displayed and the name of the farmer who had brought it in was printed in big letters right there beside that early cotton blossom. Folks admired the beautiful cotton blossom and were impressed by the winner of this coveted event. The winner was remembered from year to year. There were conversations throughout the county about who may produce that first cotton blossom.

The two farms of Robert Earl and Harvey joined but their houses were a good distance apart. The houses were close enough to see when the lights were on at each other's homes. The two men had been home from their military service for years and were entrenched in their farming. For several years the two had competed to win the contest of having the first cotton blossom. Robert Earl would see his first cotton blossom, cut it and take off to Elm City to claim his fame. Every year, when he got to the Hardware Store, he was informed that Harvey brought his blossom in before daylight that day or the day before. Harvey and others teased Robert Earl about being a late riser and that Harvey just got up earlier. Robert Earl became obsessed with getting a head start and was determined to and get up earlier than Harvey. Maybe next year he would get that first cotton blossom to Elm City. Robert Earl set his sights on what time Harvey got up. He especially wanted to get that first cotton blossom.

In the spring of 1950 Robert Earl got serious about getting up earlier. He got up at 6:00 am and went outside. He looked across the field and Harvey's kitchen light was already on. Next day, he got up at 5:30 am and looked across the field. Kitchen lights in Harvey's house were on.

Then he got up at 5:00am and same thing. Next day he got up at 4:00am and the lights were on already. Robert Earl told himself that Harvey must keep his lights on all night. He was going to find out.

The next day he got up at 3:30 am and walked over to Harvey's house expecting to see nobody up at 3:30am but when he walked to the back door, Harvey's wife came to the kitchen door fully dressed and with a bag of food for her chickens. After some greetings, Robert Earl asked if Harvey was around. Harvey's wife replied, "yes, he was here the early part of the morning but he went on to the corn field after he finished in the garden."

Pen and ink of Howard the goat by Cindy Harris.

Howard, the Goat

THE HOUSE WE LIVED IN when I was a child was a big two-story house on my grandfather's farm. The house had been the home of General William Dorsey Pender's uncle and it was probably a real show place in its day. I believe it was built about 1809. The house still stands, and my sister owns it now. There was a big porch that went all the way across the front and around the side. This porch was a good four feet or more off the ground.

On rainy days we would play underneath the house. There was a section of that porch that was the size of a door, and it lifted up to show a stairway down into a cellar. It was lifted by a thick leather strap nailed to the door. It was a pretty big cellar and was probably used for storage of root vegetables. In the side yard of this house there was a section that had thick glass covering a hole in the ground. It was mostly grown over and filled in but in the early 1940s it was still visible. Daddy said that was where the Penders stored their flowers and other plants during the winter to prevent freezing and they could get sunshine. It was an underground hot house.

Anyway, it was in the early 1940s when Mr. Howard Taft, a good friend of my father, made our lives a lot of fun. Mr. Howard lived in Columbia, NC, and was a real character. I guess he just wanted to do something one day, so he put a goat on the train and shipped him to the depot in Elm City addressed to my father. I don't remember how daddy got the goat home from the depot.

We were so excited. The goat was big as a small pony. He was brown and white and a beautiful goat — but he was still a billy goat. We named him "Howard" in honor of Mr. Howard Taft. My mother was not crazy about Howard, who may not have been the luckiest goat on some days. He roamed free like a dog and never left or tried to run away. We treated Howard like a pony. We tied a rope around his horns and got on his back and rode until he bucked us off which didn't usually take long. To add to the excitement, we would put the rope on Howard's horns and pull him out into the field and get on his back. He would run toward the porch to get under the porch, and we would jump off just before the boards hit us in the head. Then we would go under the house and pull Howard back to the field and take the thrilling ride again. We took turns and the rope would be flying behind us while we held on to Howard's horns for dear life. It was a lot of fun and Howard didn't seem to mind too much. He was a good-natured goat. At the end of the day, we would have a few scrapes and bruises and smell like little two-legged goats. Mama would make us take our clothes off outside and they were put in the wash pot and boiled. That is how germs were killed back then.

I think Mama got tired of the stinky clothes and children. Daddy built us a cart for Howard to pull. The idea was to get us a little distance from the "stinky Billy goat." This was a neat cart. He used his pocket knife to put the finishing touch on the two cedar poles and used two large iron wheels. He built the body of the cart from some boards. It was a simple dump cart but he rigged it so we could hitch Howard to the cart. It was fun for a while. It didn't take Howard long to learn how to make the cart dump us off and he did. The rides were short and the dumps often.

We finally gave up on Howard pulling the cart, but we played with the cart and with Howard for years. Howard was one of the best gifts ever, but mama was never impressed. Howard would get on the porch and run. He sounded like a horse clipping on the wood porch and mama would come out with her broom and chase him off the porch. He would stand in the yard and look at her until she went back in the house. I cannot imagine any store-bought toy being as much fun, lasting as long or smelling as bad as Howard. He was some fun goat.

William Greene on the wagon, 1920's.

Daddy Shares a Happy Memory

DADDY AND I WERE RIDING like we did a lot of days after he stopped driving due to loss of vision. Sometimes we had a specific destination and at other times we just started driving and would just drive with no particular destination. My mother said once many years ago: "I have never known anyone who likes to ride as much as William, his mother and Montress. If someone came by with an empty seat to Hell, one of them would take it."

He would say something like, "There is a road up about a mile right after you pass the old Post Office. Turn to your right and I will show you where I went with Pa when I was a boy to buy two of the best fox hounds he ever had.' He is in his 90s, so it had to have been 80 years ago that he was at this place with his grandfather. I wondered if there was anything left of the place he remembered.

We drove for miles, and he told me where to make turns. I was beginning to think we were lost, when he said, "There should be a pretty big cemetery and a two-story brick house with tall pines lining the road. Sure enough, we came to a large cemetery, and there was the road with tall pine trees. There was a big brick house that appeared to have been abandoned. He told me about the fox hounds and some of the Grandpa Wiggins stories.

He stopped talking and looked to be in deep thought. I asked him what he was thinking about. He said he was just thinking about some of his happiest days.

I asked if he would like to tell me about one of those days and he said, "Well yes, I would like to."

He said that one November day in 1936, came to mind. He said he had worked all year planting, cultivating and harvesting his crops. The tobacco had been harvested and all of it taken to the market and sold, they had had the big hog killing and the hams, tom thumbs and sausage were in the smoke house. The last harvesting was his corn crop. At that time, corn was harvested by taking a mule and wagon to the cornfield and pulling the corn one ear at a time, throwing it in the wagon to be taken to the Old Barn (corn crib) and thrown into the barn in huge piles.

He said on that cold November day he had harvested the last of his corn, unloaded it, put the wagon under the shelter, the mules in the stables and closed the barn doors. He said he fed and watered the mules and made sure all the tools were under the shelters. He started walking down the path from my grandfather's house to the house he and my mother were living in, about a quarter of a mile. All the crops were in, and he was going home where it was warm. Thanksgiving and Christmas were just days away.

When he got about half way home, it started to snow. The snow came at just the right time. He walked into the house and would never forget the smell of chicken frying and vegetables cooking or the sight of my mother smiling, my brother running around the house playing and me on a pallet where mama could watch me. (I had to be about 7 months old). He told me he had many happy days, and that day was just one that came to mind.

A Mule Named "Red"

THEY PULLED THE PLOWS AND the wagons, the disc harrows, stalk cutters and were hitched to anything way too heavy for humans. They gave their all and worked every day. The mules I knew about didn't resist — well all except one beautiful red mule named "Red." Everyone called her lazy. She would balk. She would stop in the middle of a row and sit on her hind legs. She would manage to step outside her traces. When she was working, she was slow on purpose. Red just had an attitude. Red was the last mule in the stable that the farm workers chose to work on any given day because they knew it was going to be a long hard day trying to get Red to cooperate. That meant Red was able to hang out at her stable or pasture while the other mules worked.

There was a farm about a mile from us that had several horses. If Red could manage to slip past someone or break out of the fence occasionally, she would throw her head way up in the air, kick up her heels and run like the wind to get to those horses. It was something to watch that transition. She was beautiful, shiny and fast. I believe Red thought she was a horse.

You know how people have a job sometimes that we just don't like, and we are unhappy, and it shows in our attitude and the way we behave and perform our duties. Well, I believe that was the case with Red.

I don't believe for even one minute that Red was lazy. I believe that she just hated her job.

Go See If the 'Mail Man' Has Come Yet

RURAL WILSON COUNTY, NORTH CAROLINA, was much like rural areas all over the South. It was the 1940's and we could count on our fingers the number of cars that passed the house. Some days we could count them on one hand. The one car we could count on every day was the rural mail carrier or "the mailman." One of the phrases we heard often was "Go see if the mailman has been yet."

On some days the mailman was our only contact with the world beyond the farm. Whatever anyone thinks of the United States Postal Service in today's world has no real comparison to the way the mailman was appreciated in the old days.

It wasn't that we got a ton of mail but there were some deliveries that were highly anticipated and when they were delivered it was a highlight in our day. The Progressive Farmer magazine was one of those things we waited impatiently for. That magazine may not have been so treasured by all but I remember reading it from cover to cover. It had articles about farming, housekeeping, farm animals, sewing, fashion, plants, puzzles, recipes, and advertisements for gadgets, fashions and ads that we could send off for. The Progressive Farmer was geared to the farming industry but it also had articles for the whole family.

The mailman also delivered other magazines. We didn't have much money but somehow we always had a newspaper in our house.

The Sunday edition of the News and Observer was the highlight of the day. It was a thick newspaper and had so many sections that I won't try to remember them all. The paper came early and I loved getting to it first. In good weather I would take the paper to the front porch, get in the swing and take out the funny papers first. What was an exciting time! There was a lot of articles and I spent hours reading and looking at the pictures. My dad asked that I put the sections back in order. Sadly, today that same News and Observer is about the size of a newspaper we put out when I was in high school. I believe we are missing something by not supporting printed newspapers and those talented journalists who researched and wrote the news stories and articles. I miss them. Today I read it online but it isn't the same. Maybe it was because we waited for it "until the mail man" came, and it wasn't available on computers and phones every second of every day. I understand progress and I am addicted to my cell phone just as many folks are. I am writing this on my Apple computer. I love it, but sometimes I just miss that printed newspaper and the love I had for it when, as a child and teenager, I sat on the front porch swing and read that ink-printed word.

In one of the papers I read an ad with an application to write letters to a pen pal. I mailed in my information and corresponded with a pen pal for several years. It was another reason to appreciate the mailman. Pen Pals today are equivalent to Facebook Friends and can be in touch instantly. Back then I waited for weeks to get a response from my pen pals. Instant communication has its merits but so does learning to have patience.

The Rural Mail Carrier usually had the same route for years and knew the folks he delivered mail to. He got to know who sent them mail and he also knew who they sent mail to. His workday was frequently interrupted by someone on his route who would bring him up to date on neighborhood goings on. Some of the mailmen were observant and knew a lot about each household by the clothes on the clothesline. If baby diapers suddenly started showing up on a clothes-line, the mailman assumed that there was a new baby in the house. A really observant mailman could tell if the family had new clothing. He knew how often they washed sheets. He knew the kind of under garments the ladies wore, what color their panties or bloomers were. The families didn't have a dryer back then and most got electricity in the 1940's and even then very few had dryers. Everything was on that clothesline for all to see. It was still pretty private because the only person who passed the houses every single day was the mailman.

In rural Wilson County, North Carolina, and in many rural areas too many folks were uneducated and some couldn't even read or write. Wages in Wilson County were so controlled that a person could get a job in an industry and look to different companies or businesses in an effort to make more money but mostly found that the wages were the same, almost to the penny. Education was not encouraged for many farm laborers. Therefore, many people remained illiterate in spite of the Public School System being available to everyone. Still, one thing that all the folks had equal access to was the rural mail service.

Some folks who could not read or write would wait patiently for the mailman holding a clipping from the Sears Roebuck Catalog and a few dollars in their hand. The Rural Mail Carrier became more than just someone to deliver mail. He would take that clipping with a picture, an item number and a price and count the money the child or adult had. He would complete the order for them, convert the cash to a money order. I know this sounds like a tale but it is a true picture of the way it was. I know because I saw it. Also, some of the folks would ask my mother to fill out their order form. I also know of incidents when some person who could not read or write would place a picture from the catalog, their name and their money in the mail box. The mailman would complete the order form and money order. They would receive their package so the system worked. I feel sure this was above and beyond the Rural Mail Carriers job description.

Perhaps it goes back to the Pony Express and the saying "the mail must go through." The Pony Express route was mostly between Missouri and California. Mail was transported on rail and horses in the early days. Motor cars started being used about 1901. I believe RFD stood for Rural Free Delivery. I do not remember it being free. What I do remember (1940's and early 50's) was that I could buy Post Cards from the mailman for one penny. A stamp to mail a letter was three pennies and an Air Mail stamp was six pennies. What a deal that was. I kept penny post cards to correspond with my pen pals and some cousins who lived in far away places like Virginia. Everyone who handled that post card could read my messages but I didn't have any secrets.

One of the most exciting days was when my cousin Janice and I could catch a ride to Wilson with an uncle or someone around my grandmother's store and see a Western Movie. Our favorite was Roy Rogers and Trigger. That led to being a real fan and ordering a free autographed picture of Roy Rogers and Trigger. I used one of those penny post cards to order them, and probably had every free picture he ever posed for. There was an ad in a movie magazine that showed a picture of Roy Rogers kid leather gloves with jewels on the cuff and leather fringe. They were just about the most coveted thing I ever saw in a magazine. I saved my change until I had enough to buy those gloves. I don't remember the cost but it was probably $2 or $3. I ordered those gloves and a happy day was when the mailman delivered them. I can visualize them at this very moment. They were soft kid leather, beige with red stones all around the generous cuff and the leather fringe made them perfect. I remember watching the movies and looking at Roy Rogers' gloves to see him wear those and other gloves.

The United States Postal Service is still a part of our daily life but we have so many other connections to the outside world that the U.S. Postal Service is often sneered at and called "snail mail." Yes we have email and other ways to send and receive information instantly, and I use them all. However, somewhere deep inside me I still miss the service and personal connection to the mailman and running to the mail box as he is stuffing mail into it until he saw me and he waited for me to get to his vehicle and hand me that coveted mail through his car window. The Rural Mail Carrier, in my opinion, is an unsung hero of the time. I can still hear my parents saying "Go see if the mailman has been yet."

From Left to right: Lee Petway, Tom Wiggins, Nancy Wiggins, Joe Petway, Tommy Bridgers, Bill Thorne, Pearl Petway, Nannie Pender, Mamie Petway, Kate Thorne, Billy Thorne Willey Petway.
The dogs are also named, Remus, unk behind bike, Alice and then Ring. Willey Petway is holding Ruben.

The Pender House mentioned throughout these stories was built in 1809.

Montress Greene, her father, William Greene and English Setter, Venus.

Alvis and Atlas Greene in Newport
News, Virginia during WWII.

Calvin Bridgers, son of Wright and
Martha Bridgers, smoking his pipe.
Calvin was loved by the entire Pender's
Crossroads community.

Dickie Greene,
reporting for duty, 1941.

Sam Greene,
reporting for duty, 1941.

Janice Greene Proctor and
her father, Russell Greene

Mr. Thad Moore's homeplace. Earl and Agnes Benton and daughters, Lillie Moore and Debbie occupied this house after Mr. Thad passed away.

1941 Selma and Bill Bridgers and Dell Bridgers Greene with Martha Greene Collins and Calvin's dog, Skippy.

Tom Wiggins with a few of his hounds. Photo taken in the late 1800's.

Martha Greene Collins holding a puppy, Britt Forbes and Calvin Bridgers.

William Greene and his brother, Pete Greene.

William Greene loading tobacco.

Nancy Greene Pridgen,
Beth Greene Boykin
and Cindy Greene
Harris playing "Ring
around the rosey."

Beth Greene, Cindy Greene and Dell Bridgers Greene.

William Greene with
granddaughter, Sharon
Durham and a Sweater
Gray rooster.

William Greene with Grandson, Ralph Durham
putting green tobacco in the barn for curing.

(Left to right: Alvis, Russell, Pete, Minnie, Marvin and William Greene, children of Richard and Mattie Wiggins Greene and grandchildren of Tom and Nannie Wiggins.

Conversation with My Father

(Taped and transcribed when he was 96 years old)

THIS STORY IS ABOUT A day I spent with my father — a typical visit on any given day. My dad lived his entire life on the same farm where he was born. He died at 101.

William Greene, age 96 at the Pocosin Lakes National Wildlife Refuge, Columbia, NC.

One day I drive out to my father's house and walk inside. He is sitting in his recliner, and when he sees me, he locks his fingers together across his chest and begins to twiddle his thumbs. I know twiddling his thumbs is a way of communicating to us that he has something on his mind.

"Hey, Daddy. How are you doing?"

"I'm doing fine. How about you?"

"Daddy, is there something that you need?"

"No, no."

"Is there something that you want?"

Daddy looks down at his twiddling thumbs and then glances over at his hat. "No, not especially."

"What do you mean 'not especially'? OK, that means there is something that you want."

"Well, not necessarily."

"Is there someplace you would like to go?"

Daddy's eyes light up and he stops twiddling his thumbs and glances at his hat again. "Well, one day, or sometime when somebody gets the time and can go, if somebody has time, I'd kind of like to ride down to Columbia one day."

Columbia and Little Washington are two places that he spent a lot of time. He had friends in both towns and made many day trips. He loved going places and visiting his numerous friends, but he said he always liked to be home before bedtime. Little Washington and Columbia gave him that timeframe.

"Well, when would you like to go?" I asked.

"I can go right now." His eyes light up, and he reaches for his hat. "OK, let's go."

He puts his hat on his head and this 90-something-year-old man walks to the car with some spring in his step.

When we get just a few miles from his house, he already has a story. We passed by the farm that his great grandparents had owned when the United States were still colonies. And he starts his story.

"I had a chance to buy that farm several decades ago. I never did have the money, but it came up for sale. I talked with my granddaddy and some other people and made arrangements to get the money to buy it. But XXXXXX beat me to the bid by just a few hours. That's the farm right there, and it's a nice farm. Your grandmother, who would be your great-great Grandmother Wiggins, is buried right there in that cemetery. You see the tall monument? That is hers. Grandma and Grandpa didn't really get along all that well, although they had right many children. I reckon they got along all right for a spell. No, they didn't get along, but they never divorced or separated really. What they did was they divided the house. He took half the house, and she took the other half of the house, and they divided up the children. They lived that way in the same house for many years until they died. Grandpa Wiggins was one of the children, and he went with his mother. I believe she was smarter than her husband. We called him Grandpa Billy. He was kind of a show off, and he later became a preacher of sorts. Some called him "a front porch preacher," and I remember him walking up and down the porch and talking. Don't know if it was really preaching. It sounded more like cussing. But I reckon you can preach and cuss at the same time. He did anyway."

A few miles down we reached a fork in the road. One road goes to Macclesfield and the other goes to Pinetops.

Daddy said, "You know, you can get there on either one of these roads through either Pinetops or Macclesfield, but let's take the road through Pinetops. Macclesfield was always a little richer town than Pinetops. Back in the 1920s, both towns had a baseball team. Pa helped to build a ball diamond for the boys, and he came to a lot of the games. He probably came to visit and have a few drinks with his friends down here. If I remember right, Pinetops won just about every game against Macclesfield. Pa always said the boys in Pinetops practiced more, and the boys in Macclesfield were more interested in working and making money. Pinetops was always the poorer town, and Macclesfield was known to be a little richer. Pa said the boys in Pinetops studied too much about baseball, and not enough about making a living. That was Pa's assessment anyway. I don't want to make anyone mad. Always liked to go to Pinetops. Of course, I went to both places, and when I was younger, I went with Pa sometimes to the barbershop in Macclesfield. He would get a haircut, shave and a steam bath. There was also a barber shop in Elm City that Pa went to. That was his favorite. It was called Wiley's Barber Shop and was operated by Wiley Ricks. He got his steam bath at Wiley's, too. Over there, up the path, is where old man XXXXXXXX lived. I was the registrar for Gardners Township for most of the 1940s, and I know for a fact that there was only one registered Republican voting in Gardners Township, and that's where he lived. It was like that for years."

"Things have surely changed. Some good and some bad."

"I reckon so."

"Daddy, where is the house the wagon trains met?"

"Not too far from here. Well, it was after the War Between the States, and the Yankees had taken just about everything in some neighborhoods, and it was hard to make it. Of course, that was before I was born, but the stories were told by the old timers, and I do remember some. The house you are asking about is right up a little ways on the right. It was the Reason Place (I believe that is the name). The people from miles around would come to that house and build the wagon beds and construct covers for some of the wagons, getting them ready and equipped to head out West. The women folks would come and make quilts and knit socks and make blankets and cook for the crowd. They said it was kind of a desperate act to make the decision to head out west on horse-drawn wagons. They had a lot of mules, too. Some took their families. I reckon it was hard, but some must have made the trip or stopped somewhere to settle down. Heard about some who worked on their wagons and then backed out."

"That is a lot of history made right here close to home."

"Well, sure. There is history everywhere."

"Wasn't there a house that was still standing a few years ago where the stagecoaches stopped, and the horses were rested, and the people could have a meal and get rested?"

"This house you are talking about is on what is now Highway 97. It was a good location because it was between Richmond and Raleigh. Some stagecoach travelers didn't have enough money to stop at the inn, so they made camp and rested there. They say there was a lot of folks that stopped there. It is a good-size, two-story white house with stables. The house was still standing, last time I was by there."

We continue on a day trip to Columbia.

"Daddy, that was pretty fast; we're already in Conetoe."

"Yes, we are. When you were a baby, we kept Sam because Ruby was sick a lot. Milk was hard to find sometimes, and we had two babies in the house. One was you and the other was your first cousin, or your double-first cousin, I reckon you would say. Sometimes I would drive to Coneto and buy milk at the store right over there on the right. I believe the building is empty now, but that sure was a nice man that ran that store. When I came in, he would always make sure that I had enough milk to take home to those two babies. I always felt bad because I didn't buy much else from him.

We ride for a few miles and there are more stories. He has a story about almost every crossroads and sometimes in between. He knew everybody.

"When we go over this bridge, look over to your right, and you'll see right about where Pa had a fishing cabin. He would come down and stay for a few days with some of his fox-hunting buddies. I don't know if there was a whole lot of fishing, but I'm pretty sure there was a fair amount of drinking and telling stories. It must've been some time in the 1920s that me and Marvin, Louis Forbes and the boys took Pa's car and came down to the fishing cabin with the intention of fishing. I never cared much for fishing. We got the car down to the cabin, but then we ran into a little trouble. The car got stuck, and we couldn't get it back up the creek bank and onto the road. So, all of us got behind that car and we pulled, pushed and lifted it out ourselves and got it back on the road. We cleaned the mud off of it as best we could, and I don't think we ever told Pa, but if we had it would have been all right."

Then another story, passing somewhere between Williamston and Columbia.

Daddy says, "The woods over on the left is where some Indians lived, and Howard said they were about all gone or died out some years ago. Howard was a hunting guide and knew some of them. He didn't talk much about them, but sometimes I thought he had more in common with the Indians than with the town folks. More of them lived and settled around Manteo and in the Dismal Swamp. I never knew any of them, but Howard talked about how the older ones would go to Williamston or Columbia and trade fish, animal skins and whatever they hunted for salt and other supplies. Later on, when some of the younger ones started going to town, they would get a job and not go back to the woods. Eventually nobody was left except the elderly, and they didn't like 'town.' It is hard to make changes I reckon. We are coming up on the Scuppernong River. This is the new bridge. The picture I painted for you of the eagle flying off the nest from the old dead tree was a picture of the old bridge. I have had some mighty good friends from around Columbia. Just about all of them are dead now. I still like to come to Columbia. Howard Taft was as good a friend as I ever had."

"Daddy, are we going to start telling Howard Taft stories now?

"No, no. I think we will save those for another trip. That way we get to come back."

William Greene holding, "Sweater," the gamecock
given to him by Sweater McGinnis in 1958.

Birds and Cherry Trees

IT WAS A SUNDAY AFTERNOON and like most days, my father had visitors who came to talk crops, English Setters or Game chickens. The men walked around and talked about the game chickens and which bloodlines each rooster came from. The Sweater bloodline got the most attention. He had hundreds of game chickens and could pick up any one of them and spread the toes and tell exactly what their bloodline was. He did this by hatching only the eggs laid by a specific hen that had been penned with a specific rooster. He marked the eggs, and he had a book he kept a record of all his game chickens. When the eggs hatched, took his knife and marked each chick by making small cuts in the webs of their feet. He entered these markings with the bloodlines listed in his book. Even after the chickens got old, he could spread their toes and know exactly what they were.

As they were walking and talking about chickens, they came by daddy's cherry trees. One of the men said he had cherry trees, but he couldn't beat the birds to the cherries. He said the birds don't seem to bother yours. What do you spray them with to keep the birds out? My dad told him that he didn't spray any chemicals on his cherry trees. What you do is to plant a mulberry tree close by and the birds will eat the mulberries and leave your cherries alone.

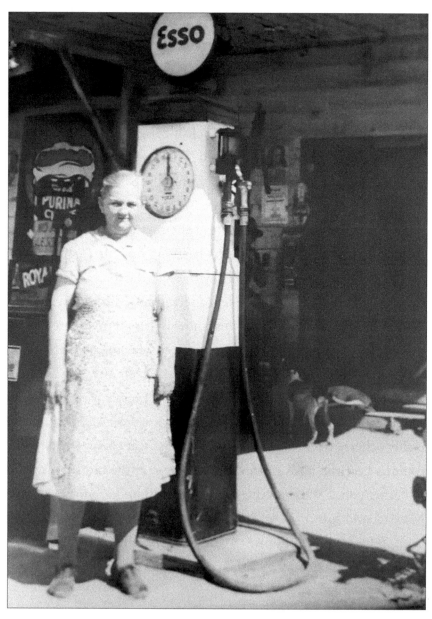

Martha Bridgers, "Miss Mothie"

Go See Miss Mothie

MARTHA SHARPE BRIDGERS, MY MATERNAL grandmother, was an asset to the neighborhood for a number of reasons, not the least of which was that she had healing powers. After my grandfather passed away, she and my aunt, Blanche Bridgers, operated the country store at Pender's Crossroads. Martha Sharpe Bridgers was "Granny Mothie" to me and to the neighborhood and beyond she was called "Miss Mothie".

Her powers have been, and still are, a mystery. I can remember asking her to tell me how she could make a burn stop hurting and all the other things she could do. She would get that look on her face that said she knew things that we would never know. Her answer was always the same, "If I tell, then I lose my power."

One of my cousins, Janice, burned her hand on the stove (a steam burn) and was crying in pain. When this accident happened, she was just across the road at Aunt Mildred's.

My aunt told Janice, "Let's go See Miss Mothie." Granny Mothie took her hand and "did her magic" and the pain stopped. The pain stopped as did the crying. Janice is still around, and we talked about this incident just a few weeks ago.

An accident around Christmas time in the mid-1940s involving fireworks, resulted in a painful burn. Granny Mothie once again looked at the burn and the pain stopped.

There were numerous cases of children getting burned by hot grease or wood burning stoves and heaters. Miss Mothie was there to talk the pain away.

This happened in October of 1959 on the same day of my great grandfather Wiggins' funeral.

A family had just moved into the house across the road from Miss Mothie's. Family was on her porch when a sudden lightning storm struck the neighborhood at the Crossroads. Unfortunately, one of the strikes hit a young black child who was in his yard across the road. Thomas Greene and Robert Greene, two of my cousins, were at the Crossroads when the tragedy occurred. The child who was struck was severely burned and his hair was smoking, and he appeared unconscious. Thomas and Robert were the first ones to reach the child. Robert attempted to give first aid. Dillard Durham, my husband at the time and the father of my children, ran across the road from Granny Mothie's and took control. He got the child in his car and headed to the hospital. Thomas went with him to the hospital. He bypassed the black hospital in Wilson (Mercy Hospital) and took this child directly to Carolina General Hospital (the white hospital). When he took the child in, they refused to treat him. He was told to take the child across town to the black hospital. Dillard insisted and said something like "Oh Yes You Are going to treat him. You can't let this boy die." They did agree to treat the young boy, and he did recover.

This was one time that Miss Mothie did not get a chance to talk the fire out. It was an emergency, and everyone is grateful for the help this child received, both at the Crossroads and the hospital. At that time, it was highly unusual for a black person to be treated at a white hospital. That is just the way it was.

Granny Mothie could brew up some tea for colds, coughs, fever, sore throat, cuts or for most of the things that happened to us.

She would soak a collard leaf in "some mixture" and tie it around our neck.

Just "go see Miss Mothie."

I remember her "talking away warts".

The warts just wouldn't go away and stay away. Doctors had removed them from between the fingers and they would return in a matter of months.

The person was in the store one day and telling Miss Mothie about the warts and they wouldn't go away and stay away. She just said, "Let me see. Let me look at them." She did and she patted his hand, said some words that nobody understood except her, and then she said, "Now, just forget about them." The warts went away and didn't come back.

She was a good business woman, a good Grandmother and was generous to all in the neighborhood.

She must have counted a zillion pennies and counted out that many pieces of penny candy. Some neighborhood child would hand her a handful of sticky hot pennies and say "I want 2 Mary Janes, 3 Tootsie rolls, 4 bubble gums, 2 red suckers, another Tootsie roll, another sucker, 1 more Mary Jane." The child would be trying to match up the number of pennies with the candy. Miss Mothie knew the family and she knew how many children were in the house and she would throw in enough candy so there would be enough for all the children. Yeah, that wasn't "magic or witchcraft." It was empathy and caring about people. She matched up the candy with the children and overlooked the few pennies she lost in the transaction. Maybe that is magic.

Montress Greene and her Molly.

Two Mules Named Molly

This is about two mules — both named "Molly".

From the time I can remember when I was about three years old, I followed my dad to the field every chance I got. I would start out running behind him and loved feeling the freshly turned cool dirt on my bare feet. When I got tired my dad would put me on the crossbars of the plow for a while and then lift me up to sit on the back of the tall black mule named Molly. Her collar had two handles for me to hold onto. My dad talked about the sights we saw. The plow uncovered arrowheads and he picked them up and would tell me what kind of rock they were made from and if he thought the Indians traded with each other. He told me which arrowheads were to hunt birds, rabbits or small game and the large spearheads were for large game like deer. He put the treasured find in his pockets. He had several shoe boxes full of arrowheads. He told us about the tobacco, the trees and corn, the birds he identified by their song.

The Molly I spent the most time with and had a real relationship with was later when I was ten years old until I was eighteen. This Molly was just a plain mule. She was white and she worked every day, and somehow she and I just clicked. It may have been the apples and carrots and an occasional handful of sugar I gave her.

On weekends the mules rested. If Molly was out in the middle of the pasture I could go to the gate, call her name and she would come to me. She would follow me out of the gate with no bridle. Then she would hold her head down for me to put her bridle on. I would get on her back, and we would spend all afternoon together. I talked to her, and it felt like she listened. She would do anything I asked of her. I know she wasn't a horse, but I think at that time Molly was exactly the pet and friend I needed. We understood each other and were friends. I don't remember who took a picture of Molly and I, but I treasure it.

To me, Molly was so much more than a beast to do heavy work. She had feelings and I believe she loved me. I know I loved her. We spent a lot of time together just roaming the fields and farm paths. I had friends who had horses, one of them had a beautiful show horse and he won blue ribbons. Molly didn't qualify for shows and won no ribbons. To everyone else Molly was just another piece of farm equipment, but to me, she was my friend.

Peachtree Switches, Cod Liver Oil, and Grover's Chill Tonic

DID YOU EVER HAVE TO go outside and break your own switch? I know I earned every switching I got from my mother. My daddy didn't take part in discipline of children much. To be fair, mama did not hurt me, but she did sting my legs a few times.

Mostly she got me for playing in a mud puddle. She would dress me and put on my shoes and socks, and I would go outside and immediately splash though a mud puddle. We were in the country, so a puddle wasn't on concrete. It was a "mud" puddle and made quite a mess of shoes and clothing. We had animals in the yard. We had game chickens, and they frequently took a dump just anywhere. We had dogs but they must have known to go away from the yard. I don't remember seeing much dog poop. Then there was Howard the Goat. Howard would drop his pills wherever and whenever he wanted. The puddles were not for splashing.

Mama was serious about cleanliness and mud puddles were way off limits. She would see me splashing and get me out and cleaned up. She warned me over and over, but I loved the water, and I was a little on the stubborn side so I would get a switching. It never hurt but would sting a little — not enough to keep me out of the puddles.

After I was four or five years old, she would send me out saying "go to the peach tree and get me a switch." I would go and carefully select a skinny switch that was really limber and even make little breaks in it to weaken it more. She would send me back to get another one.

This was in the late 1930s and early 1940s. When summer was over and the fall of the year came. Parents figured children had gone through all the childhood ailments brought on by summer like infected mosquito bites, wasp stings, poison oak or poison ivy, stepping on dried bones, stumped toes, intestinal worms and a peck or spur from a biddy hen. Those game hens did not like for us to pick up one of her biddies or even go near them. She would fly on us and sometimes a good peck or a spur would bring a little blood.

Now it was time to prepare for the fall and winter and ailments like bad colds and sore throats and coughs. To keep children healthy and ward off these things, mamas all over brought out the "cod liver oil and the Grover's Chill Tonic." We took those elixirs from September to May.

Cod liver oil was just oil, but that Grover's Chill Tonic was purple and had little white granules in it. The taste was awful, but we took it every day.

We didn't get sick much. I do remember having a cold and cough. I hope I am remembering this wrong, but I don't think so. My dad gave me a spoon full of sugar with a drop of kerosene on it. It stopped the cough. We did not have antibiotics.

Some years later, in the late 1940s, when I was going to Elm City High School and would get a sore throat, I would leave class and walk to Dr. Putney's office in downtown Elm City. It was just a couple of blocks. Dr. Putney would look at my throat and take long stick with some kind of mop on the end and he would mop my throat with "silver nitrate" and I would go back to school. I have no idea what that is but that is what he said it was. It cured the sore throats with just one treatment. I had no feeling in my throat for a day or two.

He never asked to see an insurance card. He just mopped my throat with that silver nitrate, and I went back to class.

Many of these ancient cures and preventions worked and most could be purchased at most every Country Store.

Tent Revival

I<small>T WAS THE LATE</small> 1940<small>S</small> or early 1950s. The radio was on at the country store and an excited, powerful and charismatic voice was promoting an upcoming event just a few miles away. A well-known evangelist was setting up a big tent and asking that people come to the Tent Revival if they suffered pain, couldn't walk, were deaf, had seizures, financial problems, marital issues, depression, severe headaches, confined to bed or wheelchair — and the list went on.

The charismatic voice was claiming that "healing" was just days away. He was saying that if you have arthritis to come and be healed.

The message was coming across clearly to the men sitting on Pepsi crates listening.

One would say "I have rheumatism so bad I can't get out of bed sometimes. Wonder if he can help me ." Someone else would add "My brother has seizures really bad, reckon I ought to get him over to that tent meeting." Everyone either had an ailment or had a family member who did.

There were conversations about how to get bedridden Uncle Henry to the tent revival. Questions were about the size of the tent and how much it would cost.

One man said he had been to a Tent Revival last year over near Rocky Mount and the tent was as big as a circus tent and he said he saw people come in the meeting in a wheelchair and go across the stage for the "healing" and get out of the wheelchair and walk and dance around and shove his wheelchair away.

The word spread in our neighborhood and in other parts of the county and beyond.

There was excitement about getting cured of back pain, rheumatoid arthritis, spells or seizures, severe headaches, depression, financial problems and pain of every description.

I was a young teen at this time and did not go to the Tent Meeting. I just remember some of the conversations at my grandparent's store.

I don't know if anyone got healed. I do know one of my uncles went with hope of being healed of blindness and epilepsy. He lived for years after the tent revival and was blind and took medication for epilepsy all his life.

The Tent of Healing Promises is way bigger today. The television and internet tent makes these same promises to millions in a minute.

Those farmers sitting on wooden Coca Cola and Pepsi crates just couldn't imagine what this world has come to. The party line telephones were brand new in our neighborhood about the time of this revival. Turn on your television today and you will soon hear the carnival barkers making promises of miracle medicines. It's just a bigger tent these days.

Stewed Whiskey, Featherbeds, and a Grandfather Clock

THE GRANDFATHER CLOCK TICKED LOUD enough to be heard in the next room. It was a striking clock, and the striking was loud enough to be heard pretty much throughout the house. This clock was at my great grandparents, Grandpa and Granny Wiggins, house and it lived in their bedroom. It really did seem like a living thing.

Their bedroom was a large room that had a big bed they slept on and a smaller bed I slept on when I spent the night. Both beds were fluffy thick featherbeds so dense that you could almost get lost in them.

Their bedroom also had several chairs, dressers and a big battery radio. The radio is the one my grandmother and I listened to The Lone Ranger on after dinner. The room doubled as a sitting room at times. The formal living room was at "the front part of the house" and that is where company visited.

When they blew out the kerosene lamp and went to bed it was so quiet except for that grandfather clock and it kept on ticking and striking. If it was 10 o'clock, it struck ten times. The other sound I remember was an occasional fly or mosquito would be in the room and that mosquito would sound like an airplane. There may be a couple of reasons for that. It is very quiet in the country at night, and I could hear a lot better 82 years ago.

Tom and Nannie Wiggins

In the wintertime those featherbeds felt like sleeping in a warm fluffy cloud and it was hard to crawl out from under that kind of comfort especially on bitter cold mornings.

If it was sleeting or snowing, my grandmother would be cooking breakfast on her big wood burning cook stove and my grandfather was all in her way. He would have one corner of the stove set up for making "stewed whiskey." I don't know the recipe he used.

Here is what I do remember. He had fun making it and when all the spices and whiskey had brewed enough, he would take a match from the big match box and light that brew and a big blue flame would ignite. It would burn for a bit and then just go out. When the flame goes out it is time to have a hot toddy.

Whoever was around had a cup of stewed whiskey. If several grandchildren were there, we were all given a cup with a little stewed whiskey. My first memory of this is when I was about five or six years old in about 1940 or 1941. We didn't have to drink it, but it was special that this brew was not denied to us. My grandfather said it was ok for us to have it because he burned the alcohol off. I am not convinced of that.

Grandpa and Granny Wiggins were my great grandparents. My grandmother and my father continued this tradition. That is three generations of making stewed whiskey. I don't make it. I didn't like the taste as a five year old but it sure did seem festive and it is one great memory.

Oh, By the Way

The stories so far have been about country stores and reflections of the lighter side of "Tobacco Road" and featuring the family farm. This chapter will go into the life of the people who lived closest to the dirt, the sharecropper.

THE END OF SLAVERY LEFT the big landowners with a lot of land which was useless without labor. They had to have a way to recover the lost labor.

They had the land, and the shacks but many of the former slaves went North or found jobs in the towns or cities. The people who were left for available labor were poor white and black people. Both of these groups were mostly uneducated, and most were seeking a way to survive.

The landowners had a way forward for them — farming on shares or sharecropping or tenant farming, farming on halves. No matter which term you use, it is the same — it was about cheap labor, but it was a way to survive. This continues in some places today.

The sharecropper could move his family into a shack and he and all his family provided the labor. Children as young as six or seven years old were sent to the tobacco fields to pull tobacco worms off the green leaves, pinch the heads off the worms so they won't crawl back on and eat the precious leaves. Young children pulled weeds and used a weeding hoe to chop weeds from cotton, corn and other crops.

Child labor was a part of the life of sharecropper's children. In fairness, some children on family farms were also part of the labor force. Also, some city children came to the farms to work in the harvesting of tobacco, and they also worked hard. The difference was that they could choose when to work and it was still hard work. To my knowledge, there were no Child Labor Laws to protect farm children.

Sharecroppers could grow a garden, hunt game or raise chickens or pigs for food. They planted, cultivated and harvested the corn, cotton, tobacco, sweet potatoes, grain, peanuts and other crops depending on the type of soil. They worked all year without receiving any money except for small advances on the sale of the crops. They had the use of a small garden plot to raise food.

If a sharecropper raised a few more chickens than his family could eat, he could not sell them or if his small plot grew a few more vegetables than his family could eat, he could not sell them and earn a few dollars. No, how dare he even think of such? Of course, not all land owners were this hard but some were.

At the end of the planting and harvesting season and all the crops had been sold, it was time to "settle up." The profit was to be divided as agreed. That is not how it worked for most. There were, of course, some landowners who were fair. The landowner kept the books. The sharecropper usually did not see the receipts or invoices. Many of them could not read.

Here is what happened most of the time when landowner and tenant met to settle up: The landowner would have his figures all tallied up and there was usually just enough to cover expenses — nothing to divide. Some years the sharecropper worked all year and was in the hole. The term used was "you didn't quite pay out this year." Some land owners would loan their tenant a few dollars secured by their next year's crop. Now the tenant is starting a new year with no money for his family except the few dollars he has borrowed on next year's crop.

He is obligated to stay again next year to pay back this loan which might be $20.00 or less.

It was a depressing life. This was true for both the black and white sharecropper families.

Life Wasn't Easy

IN THE 1930S AND EARLY 1940s there was no electricity in most rural areas so there was no refrigeration of food. Some had an ice box, which was a wooden box that you could put a block of ice in, and it would keep food a little cooler but not at a safe temperature. Ice was a luxury, so most sharecroppers didn't have an ice box. Without ice, it was just a wooden box.

Most houses had a well with a pulley and a rope tied to a well bucket. The bucket was lowered into the well and allowed to sink, filling the bucket with water. Then the rope was used to pull the bucket of water up to be used for drinking, cooking, bathing, washing clothes and watering animals.

On wash day it was quite a job just to "draw" the water to wash the family's clothes.

Leftover food or milk was sometimes put in the well bucket and lowered into the water to keep it cool. On hot days it wasn't much cooler in the well, but every little bit helped.

The lack of refrigeration caused some health issues. Spoiled food caused vomiting and diarrhea.

The lack of refrigeration and the lack of convenient hand washing resulted in children having intestinal worms. This condition happened in rural areas and in cities. Ingesting unwashed fruits and vegetables or eating undercooked meats or fish is usually the culprit.

Sharecropper families lived and worked close to the soil and sanitation was inadequate. Outdoor toilets and lack of convenient hand washing added to the problem.

The outhouse, sometimes called a privy, was a way to dispose of human waste and provide some privacy. They were nasty and the odor radiated outward especially on hot humid days. There wasn't enough Clorox and lime in the county to make it clean.

There was a primitive method of "flushing." Dig a new hole and move the structure to sit over the new hole. Use the dirt to cover the old hole and waste.

There were different kinds of intestinal worms — pin worms and round worms. The round worms were several inches long and sometimes so bad that a child could be seen with a worm dangling down his leg from underneath their shorts. It was not a pretty sight, and it was a difficult and uncomfortable for the affected children. The worm medications worked temporarily — until the next infection.

How do I know this? I know because I was there and saw it. I also heard the conversations at my grandparent's country store. Folks would come in and ask "Miss Mothie" about worm medicine for their children. I don't remember the name of the medicine.

Today this condition would mean a trip to a physician. That was not an option at that time for some. They had to gut it out.

Rachel

RACHEL WAS BORN IN WILSON County to parents who were share-croppers. She was a teenage girl when her parents got seasonal jobs at a tobacco factory and moved to town.

She was referred to a Job Readiness/ Job Placement class I was teaching for a nonprofit in the 1990s. The class was to assist unemployed and under employed people in overcoming or working through barriers to employment.

The barriers were as numerous as the number of people. There were about 35 people in the class and every one of these folks had a story. Some of the students had no transportation. Some were homeless or had no permanent address. Others had a criminal record or had a poor attitude, and one could not read. Some students were victims of domestic violence. Others owned no proper attire for interviews. Those with children often had no help with childcare. All of them needed help with doing a job search, completing applications, building a resume, and interviewing skills. One even told me she didn't need to look for a job because she was a Christian and if there was a job for her "The Lord would lead me to it."

Everyone had a story. It was a challenge and so much to work through.

I am just going to tell you about Rachel. She came in and was quiet. She was well dressed. At first, she didn't talk much about herself. She sat quietly but she was listening, and she took notes. After a few weeks she began to open up and tell me her background.

She was a black woman about forty years old. She was not married and had no children. She said she had a ten year old niece who was very smart and was an A student. Rachel said she would like to be a role model for her niece and help her to go to community college so she could get a job other than in the tobacco factory. She was very proud of her niece and had high hopes for her.

Rachel lived with her parents who had been sharecroppers when she was a child but gave that up and both got seasonal jobs at a tobacco factory. When the season was over, they received unemployment, year after year. It had been the lifelong cycle in her family. Rachel followed in her parent's footsteps and went to work at the tobacco factory right out of high school. She told me that nobody in her immediate family had ever done any work except sharecropping, farm day labor or seasonal tobacco factory work. She was the only member of her immediate family who graduated from high school and had taken typing but never used a computer.

Education was not deemed important for economically challenged folks in Wilson County. One way to keep labor wages low was to keep a high percentage of people uneducated.

It was the off season when she attended my class. Rachel chose not to draw unemployment this year, but she got a job with a cleaning service. The cleaning service had a contract to clean a large local bank.

Her job was to go to the bank at 5 pm and clean bathrooms.

What touched me about her story was when she said "I walk in that building every day at 5 o'clock and I watch those women leaving and I just dream about how I would love having a job like they have but I go on in and clean those bathrooms."

She signed up for a computer class. She was already a good typist and she learned quickly.

I made a call to an HR person at the bank (the bank where she cleaned bathrooms) and told her about Rachel. She didn't have a job opening right then but we kept in touch. About a month passed and the HR person called and said to have Rachel go to the temp agency and apply for a specific job and she would make sure she at least got an opportunity to interview.

She interviewed and was hired in the loan department of the bank as a temp.

Rachel called and told me how much she loved her job and now she was walking out of the bank at 5 pm and how she would like to tell some of the cleaning crew they could do what she did.

She worked as a temp for over a year and then was offered and accepted a full time permanent position. This was a big step from a sharecropper's daughter and a seasonal job at the tobacco factory.

Rachel's was one dream of a sharecropper's daughter that came true.

Gallons of Sweat and
Buckets of Tears

THIS STORY IS MOSTLY ABOUT my mama, but it applies to most rural farm women and families. Most folks who grew up on a farm have their own stories.

Mama gets up in the summertime about 4:30 a.m. and starts getting vegetables ready for our "dinner time meal". Our meals were breakfast, dinner and supper in that order. She slept about three or four hours each night. The night before she had been up until midnight shelling beans, peas, cleaning or ironing. Sometimes she may have used that midnight hour for a few minutes of quiet time.

It is amazing how she got it all done with so little to do it with. There was very little money in the house and there were no weekly trips to the grocery store. My father raised chickens, hogs and even raised pheasants for a few years. When we had pheasant for dinner, it was not served under glass, but I bet it was better than any fine dining restaurant could offer. I would pit her meals and her presentation against any restaurant ANYWHERE.

Although mama had a positive attitude, loved to sing and dance and was involved in our school work, athletic teams and in tune to our needs, she didn't hesitate to discipline us. I do remember walking in unexpectedly and could tell she had been crying. It would be quickly dismissed, and she would say something like "Let's go out to the garden and see if our sunflowers are coming up." I remember one day she said to me "let's go get the weeds out of our flowers." I was about 12 years old and had a pretty smart mouth. My reply to her was, "Why are we doing this? If we can't eat it or sell it, why are we bothering with it?" She explained that we do it because she said so and that I would learn to appreciate flowers or miss out on their beauty. At that time, I still didn't understand working on something we couldn't eat or sell. I do understand now.

The hardest year for me was the year I was fourteen years old. We were deep into the sixth week of tobacco barning season. We worked six days a week and on Sunday my father, brother and I would take out cured tobacco and take it to the pack house. A pack house is just what the name of it implies. It is a large barn that is floored and has windows. It is used to store a number of farm items. For tobacco farmers it is mostly used to store tobacco sticks and presses and grading benches in the winter. In the summer those sticks are taken to the barns and green tobacco looped onto each stick and cured in the barns. After the green tobacco has been harvested and cured it is taken to the pack house and laid out is piles that at times a ladder is needed to get to the top and keep building the pile to the ceiling. Those piles have to be carefully balanced so they won't turn over. After all the tobacco is harvested and in the pack house, the farm families and other workers meet in the pack house and start the process of getting this golden leaf ready for market. The bundles that were so carefully tied onto the sticks when the tobacco was green are untied and placed on a "grading bench" where each leaf is felt of and looked at to be placed in different piles according to the grades. This step is important because some grades bring a higher price than others when taken to the tobacco auction.

After the cured tobacco is all taken to the market and sold the pack house served another purpose. Some pack houses were cleaned, and windows washed, and lamps or lanterns were hung, and the local musicians gathered to play dance tunes and the young and old gathered for a dance. Maybe that is where the term "barn dance" originated. I am told that sometimes a piano was taken to the pack house for those dances. Legend has it that my grandfather Greene was a fun loving kind of guy and loved to swim, sing and dance and the ladies were drawn to him. Mrs. Mildred Gardner who is a cousin and was about the same age as my father told me once "The parties just didn't really start until Richard got there." He died when he was pretty young, before I was born; so I never had the opportunity to talk with him. Oh my. I do wish I had. I think I would have just loved him. These dances were a little before my time, but I heard my parents and grandparents talk about those dances and how much fun they were.

After we got the dry tobacco in the pack house we would go to the house where mama would have breakfast for us. It was usually biscuits, ham or sausage, grits, eggs or sometimes it would be cheese biscuits or cheese toast and some fruit or pancakes with sausage and maple syrup. We were always ready for that breakfast. It was a short break because the other help would be there at 6:00 am and we were part of that work force to get the tobacco out of the field and into the barns to be cured. Mama would clean up after breakfast and get her preparations started for her dinner time meal. She also went to the tobacco barn and worked. She would leave for dinnertime about thirty minutes early and have our meal on the table at Noon. It was always a hearty meal — fried or baked chicken, pork chops, cabbage, potatoes, cucumbers, squash, corn on the cob, tomatoes, crowder peas, butter beans or snap beans (green beans) or some combination of these.

Shelling beans and peas was part of summer for everyone. We shelled not only what we ate during the summer, but we picked and shelled many wash tubs full of beans and peas to be canned or frozen for the winter. There was always something to be picked from the garden or to be shelled. Even in the fall and winter the pecans and walnuts started falling and we shelled pecans and walnuts.

I remember working under a tin shelter which was in the sun and temperatures in the 90s and some days over 100 degrees. Back to the summer when I was fourteen, I was so tired that I felt I just could not keep on working. I stood under that tin shelter, handed tobacco and cried most of that day. I wasn't crying because I didn't want to work, and I was not lazy. It was not that I had something else to do or some-place to go. I was just exhausted. I am not and have never been a cry baby. Very few people to this day and I am 86 years old, have ever seen me cry, but if you saw me on that day, you would have seen me cry.

I know I was not alone. There were people throughout farming country who were just as tired. All of my family worked but I am writing my story. I hope some will write theirs. How do I know? I know because I saw them and worked alongside them. Yes, there were days we had so much fun working but there were days when we were just exhausted.

Mama was also such a great cook and gracious hostess that we had lots of company who enjoyed her meals and her and my father's company. On Holidays she hosted parties and prepared the food, eggnog or whatever was appropriate for the occasion. Folks loved to plan gatherings or parties at William and Dell's. She somehow found time to join the Ladies Home Demonstration Club for a few years. Ladies throughout the county met at each other's homes about once each month and talked about recipes, home decorating and fashion, and the hostess prepared lunch for the group. I remember hearing some of the ladies talk about how much they loved coming to Dell's house for meetings and lunch. It wasn't because she had the finest house. It was because of "who she was as a person" and it was because she was the best cook ever. I doubt if any of the others served pheasant. It didn't matter what she prepared it was always top shelf.

The unsung heroes of the farming communities are the women like my mama who were expected to do farm work, laundry, gardening, prepare meals, plus take care of children and run a household. Most of the men and boys took breaks to go to the country stores and sit on those soft drink crates and warehouse benches, gossip, shoot pool, smoke, chew tobacco and spit in the sand filled cheese box which sat just in front of the coal heater used to heat the store in the winter. Also, I did hear that a lot of the men passed by several other country stores and came to Bridgers Grocery to get a glimpse of my Aunt Blanche. Blanche got up early in the wintertime and made a fire in the coal heater so the store would be warm when her early customers came in. She got up early in the summertime to come in and make sure the soft drinks were ice cold and she swept the "dust down" off the floor and emptied the nasty sand filled cheese box, the one used by the farmers to spit tobacco juice and toss cigarette butts. She filled it with clean sand and placed it once again in front of the potbellied heater to be spat in another day.

I believe I know some of what it took to get that tobacco crop planted, harvested and prepared for market. It took "gallons of sweat and buckets of tears." We still managed to have fun.

Peddlers vs. the
Sears Roebuck Catalog

WILSON COUNTY, NORTH CAROLINA, WAS a different place back in the 1930s, 1940s and 1950s as I remember. I grew up in the country and what probably now would be called "Tobacco Road." Most people in Wilson County made their living from tobacco whether it was on the farm or businesses like grocers, clothing stores, doctors, hospitals, lawyers and almost all businesses in this county either directly or indirectly survived due to the money generated by tobacco.

In the summer and fall a little bit of tobacco money was circulating whether it was borrowed money or from the sale of the golden leaf. Everybody wanted a part of that money. It all started out in the country when the tobacco seeds went into the plant beds. There was a lot of work getting that crop ready to bring to town for sale. The growing and harvesting process started in January and continued on until after Thanksgiving when the last of the golden leaf was sold.

My story of today will revolve around the harvesting portion of that process, as we called it barning tobacco or putting in tobacco. This work was done by farm families including almost all teenagers. These families were both black and white. Children were a part of the labor required to get tobacco ready to sell. Folks worked together and had a special bond in order to survive. Mules did the heavy lifting during that time not those big monster tractors we see today. I remember Peddlers coming to our house — The Rawleigh Man and The Watkins Man were two of these peddlers. Each one would come about once a month and open up his car and show my mother some kitchen gadget and the many spices they were selling. She usually bought black pepper, vanilla flavoring and maybe a can of shredded coconut or whatever she could afford and use. Peddlers also came to the tobacco barns and spread their blankets, candy etc. on the car hoods for workers to see and purchase. Other peddlers were:

The Ribbon salesman
The Candy salesman
The Blanket salesman
The Material salesman
The Fish Man
The Sewing machine salesman
The magazine salesman
The Bible salesman

I would guess that the most successful of these would have been the sewing machine salesman and the Bible salesman.

Almost every country woman wanted a sewing machine, and the sewing machine salesman was there to offer that machine delivered on credit to be paid for in the fall after the tobacco crops were sold. They sold a lot of sewing machines, and they probably repossessed a good number of them.

The Bible salesmen were usually young men, probably college students, who were traveling on bicycles or were dropped off to walk through the neighborhoods. I don't know why but the Bible salesmen were treated special by these tobacco farmers and other rural families. The Bible salesmen were usually very clean cut young guys and were sometimes invited for meals and in some cases they were offered a place to sleep and breakfast to start rested and well fed the next day. I don't know that they were any different but in the minds of those country ladies just the fact that they were selling Bibles made them OK. We were/and are part of the Bible Belt after all. The most effective sales tool of all was The SEARS ROEBUCK CATALOG. There was a Spring Catalog, Summer Catalog and a Fall/Christmas Catalog.

These catalogs had a zillion pictures and a very brief description with a price. A lot of people in the rural south, Wilson County included, could not read or write but they could all look at that sears roebuck catalog and determine what each item was and how much it cost. There was something in there for everyone. The US Postal Service was a big part of rural folk's connection to the world beyond the farm. Most did not own a car, but the mail came every day. The rural Mail Carriers assisted some of the folks in completing their Sears order form and taking their cash, converting it to a money order and getting those catalog orders placed. The United States Postal Service was at that time a big deal in rural Wilson County.

They say that a picture is worth 1000 words and the Sears Catalog proved that to be a fact. There was just everything anyone needed or wanted pictured. The teenage boys sneaked a look at the ladies underwear section and teenage girls looked at men's underwear section. That was the porn of the time I suppose. The Peddlers came, displayed their wares and left — but that Sears Catalog kept on selling. As each NEW catalog came. The OLD edition found its way to the OUTHOUSE. You can figure its use. Just know that each page disappeared one page at a time and EVERY PICTURE WAS LOOKED AT ONE LAST TIME.

Rural Race Relations

(through the eyes of a child in the 1930s and 1940s)

THIS IS MY EARLY CHILDHOOD memory of what race relationships and life in my rural neighborhood was like in the 1930s 40s and beyond.

Much of this will revolve around the strength of women and especially black women. I am not unaware of the strength of white women as well, but this story is about a few black women who I remember from childhood. Sometimes I feel that it should be unnecessary to identify a person by their race and it doesn't always feel right to assume that a person in the story is white unless identified as black. I am not writing about the horror of racial injustice. This is about some special people from my childhood. Anyway, I will tell it as I remember it.

We lived on my grandparent's farm with both black and white neighbors. There were eight houses on the farm —-my grandparent's house and seven other tenant houses. Some were occupied by black families and some by white families. All the houses were kept in good repair. We lived in a big two story house which was built in 1809 and just a short distance from ours, a house was occupied by a black family. It was Lucille's house. Lucille was the mother of ten children. Some of these children were older than me and some younger.

Lucille:

One of my first memories was "running away" to go see Lucille and play with her children. It wasn't really running away, but it was going down the path to see Lucille without permission. When I got to her house, she was not there, but some of her children were and they were having a great time cooking cornbread in the fireplace. I was about four years old, and it was exciting. They had smut on their hands and the cornbread was blackened from the ashes and I was anxious to be a part of this fun.

We were laughing and breaking off pieces of that cornbread and knocking off ashes, eating and I was having a great time. Then Lucille comes in and kind of breaks up the party. I know now that she must have been tired from working in the field, but she took me by the hand and walked me back home. She talked to me on that walk, and I wish I could remember what she talked about.

Another time I ran away to see Lucille (I was four years old) — she was on her porch and was cleaning fish. Of course, it looked like fun and I wanted to help. She explained about the knife, but I pressed on until she finally gave in and allowed me to hold the fish and the knife. Almost immediately I cut my thumb and I still have a scar on my left thumb from that fish cleaning. She doctored my thumb and walked me home again to tell mama what happened. My mama was not upset with Lucille, but she was with me.

Another day I went to see Lucille and she was cooking" potato soup." You know I wanted some. This story tells a lot about how things really were back then. She took all of her children to another room and that left just me and Lucille in her kitchen. Her kitchen had a wood burning cook stove, a wood table covered with oil cloth, some chairs, a bench and a pie safe. Her pots hung from nails and her dishes were on a shelf.

With just Lucille and me in her kitchen, she got a chair for me and filled a bowl with some of her soup. I felt so special. I didn't understand then.

The black children and white children played together and later, we worked together. I won't even try to say that we didn't know we were different colors. Of course, we did. Lucille's children came to my house and played hop- scotch, jump rope and they taught me to use tobacco twine to make pretty designs. We played with my wagon and later with a dump cart daddy had made to be pulled by Howard the goat.

We put a string on a stick and fished Doodle Bug holes and caught bugs. We made toad frog houses in the freshly tilled soil.

As much as we played together — when I started to school in 1942 the segregation of children was real and legislated. TWO school busses came by our house. White children got on one bus and the black children on the other. We went to our separate schools. I did realize in about the 4th grade, the unfairness of our system. Our white school packed up used, torn and written on books to be taken to the black school for black children to use while we got new books. Some may deny this, but it is a fact. On occasion, a black kid would tell me "I got your spelling book."

Many years later (as an adult) I met and worked on political campaigns and got to know some of those older black school teachers from the 1940s and 50s. They were about all women and the character, the strength and life skills they embodied was just awesome. When working with people both white and black, and both male and female on campaigns, there is no doubt in my mind who is most knowledgeable of the issues, hardest working, most passionate, most dedicated and know the issues that will affect their families. It is the black women who carry that load. The black women are the ones who wake everyone up, get them out to work the polls and vote.

They work their hearts out for candidates, election after election and are made promises for their hard work — only to be disappointed again and again. They don't give up. They work the next election with the same passion while their children continued to get the used books. (Then, not now).

I do believe the absolute dedication and passion of those older black teachers in the 1940s and 50s could and did make up for not getting new shiny books. Those ladies provided way more than a new book.

I will fast forward about 20 years. I had gotten married, and a baby is on the way. I reached out to Lucille. All of her children had moved on and were doing well. I told her that I was having a baby and didn't have any idea what to do with a baby and would she please come and stay with me when I came home from the hospital. I probably pressed just like the four year old wanting to clean the fish.

She was at my house when I brought my son home. I had no idea what to do with a baby. I never even liked playing with dolls.

My son was a healthy and happy baby, and I was terrified of him — afraid of doing something wrong. I made a deal with Lucille. I would cook for her and do everything around the house if she would make sure the baby was taken care of. She humored me for about a week and then she gradually turned over the care of my baby to me. She had been at my house for about two weeks, and I loved having her there because I thought she knew everything. She told me she needed to go home. I begged her not to leave until my son's umbilical cord came off. I will never forget her reaching down and saying, "You mean this? It's past ready to come off." And it was GONE! She told me that taking care of a baby was simple. She said "Keep him fed, keep him clean and love him. That's all he needs." She was right. I miss Lucille

Aunt Ada:

Another black woman on the farm was Aunt Ada. As a child I thought she was some kind of Holy woman. She was very tall, (probably close to 6 feet). She was slim and stood straight and confident. Her skin was really light, and her hair was wavy. She ALWAYS wore long white dresses with long sleeves even when she worked in the field. Her dresses never looked soiled. They were starched and white. Her features looked Indian. She didn't talk much but when she did — everyone listened. In my young eyes she really did have an aura around her. She went about her life at her own pace and knew about plants, trees, herbs, crops, how to make medicines from leaves, roots and plants. No one seemed to know how old she was.

She said she had raised her children and had "taken in" and raised twenty-one other children. She said someone would bring a baby to her and tell her it was her grandchild. She said some were and some were not, but she raised them all the same.

I remember seeing her and it was a feeling (for me as a child) that she was a God of some kind with that long white dress and that aura around her.

Can anyone imagine what strength it took to take in and care for that many children?

Her presence was not just seen but it was felt. The world is a richer place for her having passed through. I have a perfectly clear picture of her in my mind.

And Then, There Was Mag:

Mag was the manager and enforcer of the neighborhood. She was feisty and bossy (in a good way) and she knew exactly how to maneuver the racist folks she encountered. It was like "people poetry." She was a genius when it came to people skills. It wasn't exactly like she manipulated people, but she was a gifted salesman. Unlike Aunt Ada, Mag talked a lot.

Mag worked on the farm, but also had a business on the side. She found time to work in the homes of the white neighbors. She either kept children or did domestic chores for a little money (nobody had a lot). Mag worked in most of the white people's homes. She was social, listened and gave advice freely, and through her interactions and observations, she knew all the gossip. She knew most everything about all of them. She knew their secrets and she knew how to gather the things she needed for her children. Mag just asked for what she needed, and she saved her money.

The people who lived on my grandparent's farm had access to most everything needed. There were big gardens with all kinds of vegetables and fruit trees, berries and pecan and walnut trees. Vegetables were canned for winter and fruits were canned or dried.

My Grandfather raised corn and wheat and took it to be ground into flour and cornmeal. He had a big barn that housed barrels of flour, meal, molasses, sugar and corn syrup. He raised cows, hogs, chickens, guineas, and turkeys. There was always meat in the smokehouse and there were eggs, butter and always a supply of liquor (made right on the farm). The people (black and white) who lived on the farm had access to food. They all helped to grow, harvest and preserve it. My grandfather even flooded a field near the creek and raised rice for a few years.

Getting back to Mag, she loved to fish at the farm pond, and you would catch her sitting on her stool fishing on a regular basis. After my grandfather died in 1959, my uncle inherited the portion of the farm with the pond. He decided to re-stock the pond. He went to the pond one day and Mag was fishing. He told her that he was restocking the pond and she couldn't fish there. She looked at him like he was crazy. He told her again. She told him to move on and stop scaring the fish. They argued a bit in a good hearted way and Mag told him that she fished in that pond before he was born and she would keep fishing and for him to run along and leave her alone. Mag told me she kept fishing.

A story Mag told me about her husband: She said he "got religion" and started going to church two or three times a week. She was at home with a house full of children. She said she got curious about what was going on at the church and decided to attend the service one night. Mag said the preacher started talking and got more excited and louder and everyone in the small congregation started shouting and then they were falling on the floor and talking a strange language. She said, "I was watching them close, and I figured out one thing for sure: they weren't on that floor looking for Jesus."

She was such a joy.

Mag had twelve children. All of her children went to college except one who was a musician. They became teachers, an RN, school Administrators, Chief of Police in a large city and all were successful. They purchased a lot and built Mag a nice, brick home for her old age in her same old neighborhood. I would drop by to see her sometimes and it was always a fun visit. She always had stories. She usually had something cooking and I remember how good her collards and cornbread were.

After my children were in school Mag would call me and say "I want to go to your house tomorrow. Pick me up before you go to work." I would say ok. She was Mag and I was trained as a child to do what she said. She would be at my house all day while I was at work and my children were in school. I don't know what she did all day. I didn't ask her. She did not need to work. Her children took care of her very nicely. Sometimes when I got home, I knew she had made herself a little drink and was feeling pretty good.

Mag was the same as when I was a little girl. She would say to me "I am ready to go home. I am going to pour me a drink to take home. You have two cans of Comet, and I don't have one, so I am taking this one," She was Mag, so it was ok.

My children loved Mag just like I did. I can remember my children seeing Mag at the Mall and them running to her and her running to them for big hugs.

While all of this is happening on a personal level, the cruel racist atmosphere lived on. White neighbors were busy building private schools in the 1960s. Some of my neighbors were active in building the private segregated schools and were determined to recruit white children to go to their new private school. This was taking place when my son was in the first grade in Public School. I was pressured to move him to a private segregated school, but I stood my ground, and he remained in Public School. This is one decision I have never regretted. Some parents even started home schooling their children to keep them segregated. The school my son attended was integrated with few issues.

Frozen Pond (or Hog Waller) 1946

THE WINTER HAD BEEN COLD for a long enough period of time for any standing water to freeze solid. Me, my brother and two cousins had been going into the edge of the woods to this frozen pond and sliding or skating on the ice. It wasn't quite as glamorous as a frozen pond. It was actually in the middle of a fenced in hog pasture which encompassed the edge of the woods. It was more like a deep "hog waller" that had frozen over, and it would be used by the hogs again as soon as it thawed. The hogs were too smart to walk on it like we did. It was fun and I felt sometimes as if I could go straight from that frozen hog pasture to the Ice Follies.

We would run and slide across the ice. What fun that was. There was a fallen tree on one side of this pond, and we would get a running start and slide into the log. After several days of the ice skating, it must have started to warm up and especially right in the middle of this pond where there was an opening through the trees and the sun was shining through. It felt like we were in a spot light. I did not realize it, but the ice was getting thinner. I was a little younger so the boys kept telling me how great I could skate and telling me to slide again and again across this ice into the log. I feel sure I thought I was skating great because they kept cheering me on and I kept trying to make the perfect slide. I was sliding across the pond and just as I crossed into the sunlight or spot light, the ice broke and I fell through the ice into the water up to my waist. The boys were laughing because the scene played out just like they planned. I must have been cold, but I was so mad at them, I don't remember being cold, but I do remember being mad. We were about a quarter mile from the house so by the time I got home my clothes were frozen solid. I don't remember any spankings from this incident — but I do not test ice to this day.

Teeny Comes to the Farm

THE YEAR IS 1950. TEENY came to live with us on the farm. His parents were friends with my parents, and they visited us often. Teeny's dad remarked that he wished his boys behaved as well as we did. Teeny and his older brother were constantly in trouble. They threw rocks at street lights and got into fights but were not "bad."

One day, in his frustration, Mr. Richard, Teeny's father, had to go to his office and he must have had a particularly trying day with his boys because he tied them to a tree in the yard and told them he would be back shortly. He told them to be there when he got back and stay out of trouble. Well, they must have gotten bored, and the rope was long enough for them to get into more trouble. They set an outbuilding on fire. Of course, neighbors called the Fire Department. Mr. Richard was called at work and rushed home to find his garage on fire. I can imagine it was a confusing scene. The garage is burning, and the Fire Dept. is there along with the Rocky Mount police and two teen aged boys are tied with a rope to a tree. Shortly after the fire Mr. Richard asked my parents if Teeny and his older brother could come and live with us and work on the farm for the summer. My mother agreed to take Teeny who was 14 years old at the time but that she could not agree to take the older brother.

When school was out in the spring of 1950 Teeny's parents brought him, his blue jeans, T-shirts, and work shoes and left him at our house. Teeny who was used to getting attention in a negative way like throwing rocks at Rocky Mount street lights or fighting or burning is father's garage landed in a much different environment. He was there to work and to behave. My mother made it clear that he would be treated and disciplined the same as her children and she meant it. On the first day, he tried my mother's patience, and she gave him a good explanation or "talking to" and popped him on the butt with her trusty yard stick and he is a 14 year old boy. Teeny was shocked and pulled away from her sand said, "You can't hit me. You are not my mama." My mama agreed with him that she was not his mother but as long as he was living with us, he would behave, or she would deal with him the same way she did with us. Then she sent him out to pick peas the rest of the afternoon.

There is a story for every day on the farm and there were dozens of characters to write about, but this is about Teeny. There were two bicycles at our house and three teenagers, so we took turns. One Sunday afternoon my brother and Teeny had been riding the bicycles for what seemed to me like a really long time as I patiently waited for one of them to get off. They kept riding and part of the time they rode around and around the house. I tried to tell them it was my turn, but they ignored me. Daddy had made a drain ditch about 8 inches deep and lined this ditch with concrete so it would drain out into a field. We had put boards across the ditch as a bridge to ride the bicycles across. When my patience was gone, I waited for them to be out of sight of the ditch, and I moved the boards. They came flying around the corner of the house and rode across where the boards had been. The bicycles hit the ditch with a thud and both boys came off and I had two bicycles the rest of the day.

Teeny was treated the same as we were and worked and was a member of our family for the summer and he learned to behave. His parents visited on some weekends and would ask my mother how was

Teeny doing and I remember her saying "I do not have any trouble with Teeny."

Fast forward to The Year 1980. It has been thirty years since those summers on the farm. Teeny had graduated from school and had become quite successful. He came by to see my folks regularly over the years.

1980 is the year my mother died. Her death was the biggest loss that any of us had ever had. She was the center of the family and the one who kept it all together and we looked to her for answers. She had touched so many lives in a positive way and the visitation at the funeral home evidenced just that. They had opened up an extra room and there were people in the hall. During this visitation, someone came to me and asked who was the man standing alone in the hall and was crying. I went to look and saw that it was Teeny, so I went over and gave him a hug. He was visibly shaken, and he said to me, "You know, I owe my life to your mama. The woman lying in there saved my life. Ham (his brother) was not so lucky. He was in and out of jail and died a young man. I owe everything I have to her." He told me that my mother had gotten him on the right track and that if she had not taken him in when she did that, he would have ended up just like his brother, Ham. He said he owed it all to her. I know Teeny came by to see my folks regularly over the years and I hope he told her this while she was living. I feel sure he did. He had come a long way since that spring day in 1950 and I believe he was experiencing grief and memories of those summers spent with my mother.

Tom and Nannie Wiggins

"Miss Nannie"

MY GREAT GRANDMOTHER, (GRANNY NANNIE) was petite. Most of the ladies of her status were dressed in their lacy dresses and drinking tea with friends and had help to do their housework and serve their tea. That was not my Granny Nannie's choice. She dressed in simple dresses and always wore a black and white checkered apron and bonnet except when she dressed up to go to town. Here are just a few of the things I remember about her:

Her husband, my great grandfather (Grandpa or Pa). was 6' 4" and had a powerful presence. He was called " The Big Cheese" by some who were probably a little envious.

"Granny's Corset." Although she was tiny, she got up every morning and put on her corset. It was the kind I saw later in the movie Gone with the Wind. It had strings that were pulled tight. Sometimes when I was at her house, she would ask me to "hold a string or pull one."

"Dinner Bell." It was on the back side of her house between the mule stables and the cow pasture — just at the mouth of a path that went all the way past tobacco barns and across the pasture. This Dinner Bell was large and loud. It was mounted on a tall wooden frame taller than the top of the barns. It had a rope attached to the bell that hung down the side of the frame and was secured to silence the bell.

This bell alerted the folks working in the fields that it was "dinner time." Back then there were three meals per day, and they were

"Breakfast, Dinner and Supper."

Every day at 11:00am she went out and untied the bell and tugged the rope over and over and the bell was heard all over the neighborhood. It told the workers it was time to take a break and come home for dinner.

Then at 1:00 pm, she rang the bell again — time to return to work. Not many folks had watches.

Hitching up the Mules:

Granny Nannie was on top of how everyone was treated and that included the mules. When the tenants came to the mule stables about sunrise, Granny was there to make sure each mule had their right bridle, bit and collar. The wrong bit could cause mouth pain as the wrong collar could cause shoulder injury.

She checked the water and hay and made sure each mule was in their own stall at night. And saw that the stalls were clean. Yes, they had access to the pasture.

She cooked big meals and even between meals there was some great treats. If you lifted the white table cloth there was all kinds of goodies — cold biscuits, Apple Jacks, cornbread, damson preserves, peach, pear preserves, molasses, country ham, sausage, sweet potatoes, pickles, pies, etc.

She always had food for anyone. It wasn't Twinkies or chips, but it was way better.

Turkeys, Chickens, Guineas, Cows, Hogs:

Granny Nannie watched over and cared for all the above. She gathered the eggs and built tobacco stick pens for her setting hens. When biddies were hatched, she took the hen and biddies from the nest and put them into the tobacco stick pen. These fowl were important because they were part of the food supply for all who lived on the farm.

The guineas kept the garden free of bugs and the yard free of fleas, ticks etc. They were also part of the food supply. I remember her making guinea pastry (like chicken pastry). I do remember the Guinea meat was darker than chicken.

Cows: There was usually at least one milk cow and a calf to be cared for. Granny either milked the cow herself or made sure they were milked on time. Then she used the milk to make butter, buttermilk and cream. She had a wooden churn and I remember her turning the crank. She would let us children churn sometimes. The butter was put in a mold that left a flower design on the butter.

Hogs: She kept a watch over the hogs and especially the sows, and when little pigs were born, she made sure the sow's first meal after birthing pigs was several ears of red corn. I don't know why the red corn. Note added: I did Google this and found that red corn has 20 per cent more protein and 300 per cent more anti-oxidants than yellow or white corn. They did not have Google. How did they know this in the late 1800's?

My great grandfather was kind of a sport. He had a dozen or more fox hounds and enjoyed fox hunting. He had a fishing cabin on the river near Columbia and he had lots of visitors and friends who liked to come out to the farm and have a drink and conversation with Tom.

Granny Nannie made it clear that she didn't want the drinking and cuss words in her house. So Grandpa built a one-room house near the pecan trees in the side yard. It had a heater, table and chairs, a settee, cupboard, a bed and was stocked with whiskey for his friends. He called it his "Office."

I remember when I was in the first grade Granny Nannie and Grandpa came to Gardner's School and picked up my brother and me to take us to the Wilson County Fair. The driveway around back of the school had school buses on one side and a telephone pole on the other. Grandpa was set to drive his huge red Hudson automobile between the busses and pole. Granny said "Tom, I don't believe there is enough room to get between them." He assured her he could and proceeded through. Yep, he made it but there were scratch marks on both sides of his car. She didn't say, "I told you." We went on to the fair.

Snuff. Granny liked her snuff and usually had a snuff brush tucked in her mouth. She kept her snuff box in her apron pocket. When her snuff brush supply got low, she would take some of us children to the woods with her where she located the right kind of tree (not sure but I believe it was black gum or beggar weed) with new growth. She would cut a few twigs and we would go back to her house and we children chewed the ends of the twigs until it was frayed. She trimmed the freshly chewed brushes and picked the ones she wanted and gave us the rejects. She mixed cornmeal and sugar and parched it into a sweet golden mixture for us to dip. She used one of her old tin snuff boxes to put parched meal in and we used our snuff brushes to dip the sweet treat. It didn't take much to entertain us. My mother was not impressed.

Snuff had other uses. When we got a bee sting, stepped on a dried chicken bone in the yard or stumped a big toe on a tree root Granny Nannie would reach a finger into her jaw and come out with a plug of the snuff and slap it on the sting or wound. Sometimes she would tie on a rag. We survived.

Granny Nannie cooked big pans of cornbread, or "dog bread" for Grandpa's fox hounds. I don't know if they also had commercial dog food. I think they must have. It was fun to get to her house before she put the dog bread in the oven and write my name in the uncooked mixture. After it was cooked my name would be golden brown on the big pan of dog bread. We were so easily entertained.

There was a fireplace in her kitchen and a slop bucket sat on the brick hearth. Any food scraps or peelings went into that slop bucket. Also, after she washed her dishes, she put the last of that dish water into the bucket. Every morning and every evening someone took the slop bucket to the hog pen, and it went into the trough with the hog feed. Nothing was wasted, not even dish water. I still wonder why the soapy dish water. I feel sure there was a reason.

Some things I remember and can still hear her saying:

"Aw, Shaw"

"Lordy Massy"

"Do not put anything in your ear except your elbow"

"Tarry up and destroy"

"If you keep drinking vinegar, it will dry up your blood"

Let's go see if we can gather some "broom straw"

"Much Obliged"

"Taint' Worth While "

"Let's sit still and be quiet while the Lord does His work "

Granny Nannie died in July of 1951. She is still missed.

Bill and Selma Bridgers with niece, Martha Greene and Calvin's dog, Skippy.

WW2 Memories

I WAS FIVE YEARS OLD in 1941 and remember my parents listening to Gabriel Heeter and H. V. Kaltenborn on the radio every evening to get War news. This was before our rural area had electricity. We listened to a battery-powered radio and my folks read by a kerosene lamp. Our house was heated by a wood burning heater and cooled in the summer by a couple of huge beautiful oak trees. I can still remember the smell of the burning logs and see my dad stoking the fire and how cool the shade of an oak tree can be on a hot summer day.

Rural Electrification got us hooked up in 1942, the year I started first grade. For most of that year I read Dick and Jane books by a kerosene lamp. I did not understand all about the war, but I knew we were fighting Hitler.

At my grandparents store just down the road a piece, the men came to the store to socialize, have a beer, shoot a game of pool, gossip a little, talk about baseball, farming and the War. When news of the war came on the radio, everyone stopped talking and they listened. Most of our neighbors had a family member serving in the military and stationed overseas fighting Hitler and the Nazis. Neighbors sent mail and packages to the soldiers. My grandparents always contributed something from the store to add to the packages (chewing gum, socks, hard candy, a pocket knife, or Bicycle playing cards).

After the 1941 attack on Pearl Harbor by the Japanese the tension was even greater when my parents listened to the news, and it was the same at Granny Mothie's store. The descriptions of that attack were vivid. The pictures on the newsreel at the movie theaters got even more violent and scary.

At school we made cards from construction paper and wrote messages of thanks and mailed them to the soldiers. Everyone was a part of this war effort to stop Hitler and the Japanese. 1942 through 1944 school children helped. We picked up scrap iron on the farms — nails, plow points, old wheels and anything metal. We took these pieces on the school bus to be picked up by the Defense Department to be used to make weapons, equipment and bullets. It was everyone's war or that is how it felt.

About this same time, I remember airplanes dropping leaflets in our neighborhood. These leaflets were in yards and the fields and just everywhere. They gave information about a "blackout." Everyone who picked up a leaflet was asked to tell a neighbor to turn off all lights on a specific date. I remember my dad covering a window in one room on that night of the blackout making sure no light could be seen from outside. I don't know the reason for the blackout, but I understood it had something to do with the Germans not being able to locate some military bases. We were at least 40 miles from the nearest military base.

Rationing of food, clothing, gasoline, sugar, milk and other items was a part of the war effort too. For instance, we had to have a stamp authorizing the purchase of a pair of shoes. Stamps were needed to purchase most items. These stamps had no monetary value. They just gave folks permission to buy a pair of shoes and gave the merchant permission to sell them.

The Crossroads saw many families move to Newport News, Virginia, to work at the Ship Yard. Several of my uncles and neighbors made this move. It was an important part of the war effort.

We visited family in Virginia during this time and on one of those visits, I remember going to the Ship Yard to see one of the ships. We knew these ships were being used to fight Hitler and I felt proud that my family was doing this important work. Most of the families who made this move came back to the Crossroads after the War was over, but some stayed and their children and grandchildren are there still.

Life went on during the War. Crops were planted and harvested. Tobacco ties were held in the barns and took on a party mood. Neighbors would gather at each other's barns to help get the to-bacco ready for market. The host farmer served boiled peanuts, soft drinks or other snacks. I remember watching the adults laugh and have fun while getting work done. They brought their children, and it was playtime for us as well. There may have been alcoholic beverages available, but I don't remember seeing it.

Movies were a big thing, the County Fair came in the fall, people gathered and partied, babies were born, there were dances, night clubs (even in small towns), supper clubs, base-

Selma Bridgers with daughter, Betty

ball, evangelists set up their big tents and promised healing for what-ever illness or condition folks suffered. People still had fun. Soldiers came home on leave and were celebrated. The 1940s music (to me) is still some of the best. I remember going to the Carolina Theater in Wilson and watching the Newsreel between shows. It would show scenes from battlefields of tanks blowing up, soldiers running into fox holes, bombs exploding and other horrors. I heard it on the radio, but those Newsreels were hard to forget.

Underneath the gaiety there was worry about the War, our soldiers and our future, but that worry came to an end in 1945. Hitler was defeated and gone. Our soldiers were coming home.

Neighborhood men still gathered at the country store, swapped stories, took their chances on a punch board, chewed tobacco, smoked cigarettes, shot pool, gossiped, had a Coca Cola or a beer, spit tobacco juice into the sand filled cheese box, and listened to Gabriel Heeter and H. V. Kaltenborn talk about our Victory.

1940 Orange Crush

THERE ARE SOME MEMORIES THAT I am not positive if I actually remember or if I heard the incidents talked about. It was in the fall and just about dark. Daddy was walking to my grandmother's store, and I was following him as usual. He had told me to go back to the house, but I was determined to go to the store. I liked the multi-colored lights around the store shelter, and it was just a cool place. This store was a gathering place for the neighborhood farmers. It was a social place and a kind of therapy for the men who sat on the "drink crates" and swapped their stories — some true and some not, but they talked and got things off their chests. The neighborhood women came to the store also, but they came mostly during the day to get groceries, material, thread, canning supplies and have a small Coca Cola. The women also enjoyed catching up on gossip and adding a little tidbit here and there. In the evenings most of the women were at home cleaning up after dinner, tending to children and making preparations for their meal for the following day.

On this particular day as I followed daddy and did not go back to the house like he asked me to do. I just kept following him. He was a fair distance ahead of me when he met Mr. Kindred who had been cutting wood and was on his way home (walking). This man was wearing an oversized floppy hat, large rubber boots and a big overcoat and he had an ax over his shoulder. He could have been the "ax killer." Anyway, daddy told him "Montress is following behind me, and I told her to go back to the house. See if you can scare her so she will go back." So, Mr. Kindred walked toward me and stepped directly in front of me and said in a gruff loud voice "Go back to the house." I looked at him and kept walking. Then he drew the ax back and slammed it down into the dirt in front of me like he was angry and told me again to go back to the house. I did not go back to the house. I did not run. I did not speed up or slow down. I kept walking toward the store. I guess I just didn't scare easily. Perhaps a less determined or less stubborn child would not have gotten an orange crush that night, but I did. Daddy told me this story (or referred to it) many times over the years. Not saying I was the smartest 4 year old, but I got the orange crush.

My mother did say that every Greene she knew must have a magnet up their butt that drew them straight to the Crossroads.

Disappearance of the Family Farm

THE NEIGHBORHOOD I GREW UP in was made up of numerous family farms. My grandmother's store was at a point where five country roads met in her store yard. All five roads led to her store. On each of these roads there was a number of small family farms. These farms were mostly 75 acres to 150 acres in size and this acreage provided a good living for the family who lived and worked their farm. No, they did not get rich or accumulate great wealth, but they lived well. Each farm raised livestock including chickens, pigs, cows, mules, turkeys, etc. They also grew vegetables and had fruit trees. In other words, most of the food for the family and the livestock was raised or grown on the farm. Their living was hard but rewarding work. They took care of the land and did not allow it to be overused or for the topsoil to wash away. They owned it and took pride in it.

Children in these families took pride in the farm also and at least one child or grandchild from each family stayed on the farm and took over the farming at the retirement or death of parents. These children also had a good life and were able to raise their family and provide education. I will not try to say to you that farm life was without its issues. Farmers were at the risk of losing crops due to dry weather, hail storms, crop disease, drowning from heavy rains and other elements. Most small farms did not have an abundance of cash so many took advantage of loans made to farmers by Production Credit

Association. This agency made small loans to farmers who used their anticipated income from the crops the coming year as collateral. The system worked well because farmers could borrow the money to get buy seed, fertilizer and equipment to grow that crop.

There was an attitude of pride in the operation of these small farms. There was a sense of security for farm families. And, yes, there were some very large farms and these large thousand acre (or more) farms had sharecroppers to provide labor. The owners of these large farms, for the most part, lived away from the farm and this was quite different from what I am talking about as a family farm. Many of the farmers in our neighborhood met daily at my grandmothers store. They sat on a Warehouse Bench or on wooden Coca Cola or Pepsi crates and rocked back and forth gathered around a potbellied heater with a cheese box filled with sand in front of it. This cheese box was used as a spittoon for those who chewed or dipped and as an ashtray for those who smoked. They rocked back and forth and listened and waited for their turn to get into the conversation. These folks had patience. They talked about farming, family, newborn children or grandchildren, marriages, affairs, new varieties of seed, best fertilizers for each kind of soil, the amount of rainfall, baseball, car races, who had the first cotton blossom, tobacco worms and suckers, chewing tobacco, beer, newfangled farm equipment, the War and news, stories from letters received from family members who were serving in the military, but mostly it was about farming with baseball a close second. These folks knew they were not getting financially well off, but they also knew there was security in that they owned a small farm on which they could make a good living and have peace of mind. They also knew there were more financially rewarding jobs in the big cities, and some had left and taken these jobs. However, the family farm was there to catch them if the big city life wasn't what they thought.

Farm life was a good life.

As some of the children and grandchildren moved away from their farms, another farmer would rent the crop acreage for a small portion of the value of the crop because of labor. My understanding is that the farms in the Western US and Midwest were very large consisting of thousands of acres. These farms also used the crop insurance and loans to operate. I had moved away from the farm but visited my parents often. I can't tell you how it happened or anything about the negotiations. All was going pretty well and small family farms were doing nicely.

Fast forward a bit December 1985. I remember sitting with my father in his living room watching the news. My father got very quiet as he watched on the nightly news as the President signed a farm bill. At the time I was not into what was happening on the farm or in Washington up close, but I did watch my father react to the signing of that bill. My father never used curse words or raised his voice, but I remember him saying and I quote: "That S.O.B. has just destroyed the family farm with the stroke of his pen." My father rarely reacted negatively to anything, but the signing of that bill was one of those rare occasions. If I remember correctly, what this bill did to small farmers was: Get Big or Get Out. Small famers with 100 acres could not compete with the big farms with thousands of acres (which became Agri Business). Production Credit no longer loaned money to the small farmers to operate and government subsidies were for Agri Business. Small farms did not qualify. Small farmers could not borrow money so they leased their land to big operators who would rent dozens of small farms and qualify for all the perks of the larger Midwestern farms. The lease for the farm was not enough for the small farmers to exist so most of them had to sell the farm to survive. The neighborhoods that once had small farms with the owners living on the farm taking care of the land and the home, they lived in are mostly gone. The neighborhood reflected the good life. Today the same neighborhood has changed. The farm houses are now either gone or falling down. Some of the farms are now housing developments. This is what happened to the Family Farms that we read about in farm magazines like *Progressive Farmer. Get Big or Get Out.*

When the Creeks Ran Clear

In the 1940s, I have memories of spending a fair amount of time at two bodies of water that were either on or near my great grandfather's farm. One was a fish pond and the other was a creek which joined the property line. Us children, but mostly me and my cousin Janice, who is a few months older than me, spent a lot of time exploring the farm, woods, creek and fish pond. The creek was one of the favorite places for us to spend time playing and being cowgirls, detectives or whatever characters we were for any given day. In most of the area along the creek bank was clear of underbrush and there was plenty of space to walk on the bank without obstruction. Sometimes we crossed the creek, and the water was a different depth according to the amount of rainfall but it was about two or three feet deep at the places we chose to cross. There were places it was deeper. I can remember vividly looking at our feet on the creek bottom and seeing as clearly as if looking through clean clear glass. We saw fish swimming around near us and we watched the turtles. The water was flowing at a fairly rapid rate and was crystal clear. After a heavy rain the creek currents were stronger. The creek was one of the places that if we had asked permission to go, the answer would have been "no." I am not advocating for children to do what they know would be forbidden but I am so happy I have a memory of the creek when it was a beautiful place. I do remember on occasion there would be someone fishing from the creek bank and since we knew everybody in the neighborhood, we were not encountering strangers. All they asked of us was to please do not scare away the fish.

The other body of water that attracted us was grandpa's fish pond. He had a dam built on one end of the pond and the water was pretty deep at that point. It was a fairly large pond and it, too, provided a place for neighbors to fish. Grandpa kept a row boat tied to the small dock near the dam. There were several trees in the pond which, to us, made it easy to pretend we were on a tropical island paradise. It was fairly easy for us to untie the boat, get the oars and shove off into the pond. We would sometimes play like we were solving a crime and create a situation or crime scene that today would seem ridiculous. It was childhood fantasy, and it was fun to row around the pond.

Nobody knew where we were unless someone happened to be on the bank fishing. There were no telephones to check on our where-abouts. During this time, I had three grandmothers living within walking distance of my house and three more great grandmothers within a few miles. There were aunts, uncles, older cousins and family as well as numerous family friends living in this neighborhood, and it was a great neighborhood. I guess everybody thought we were at someone else's house. The pond water was not so clear. It was still water, and we might see a turtle or a fish near the surface but what lay on the bottom of the pond remained a mystery.

There were reasons the creek was clear 70 or 75 years ago. First of all, there were ditches on either side of the dirt road and the State of NC kept those ditches cleaned out so the water could flow to the creeks. Also, each house or barn had a path off the road. Every path had a large tile underneath for the water to flow freely under the path. These tiles were also kept clear of debris. I don't know what the big piece of equipment was called that cleaned the ditches, but we called it a "road drag." Mr. Cook from Elm City drove the road drag and kept the water flowing and the dirt roads in good condition. As children, we were entertained for a while watching Mr. Cook clear out the ditches and scrape the dirt that had washed off the road into the ditches and put it back on the road where it stayed until other rains washed it back into the ditches. I have been by that same creek over the years and recently. The creek no longer flows. It is still water and covered with a green scum. There is no movement and there is no way to see anything beneath that green scum. The farm paths have now become driveways and most of them have no tiles underneath, so the water flow is stopped. The roads are paved now so there is no reason for the "road drag."

Back in the 1940s and 50s we did not use chemicals for everything on the farm crops. For instance, now there are chemicals to kill weeds, another to kill tobacco worms, another to kill the suckers on the tobacco. Back then we chopped the weeds with a weeding hoe, we pulled the tobacco worms off the leaves by hand and pinched his head off so he wouldn't crawl back on the tobacco. The suckers were pulled off by hand. These chemicals and many more are now being washed over the soil and on to the creek contaminating wells, ponds and soil on the way and the result is a creek covered with green scum.

No child will be playing in the creek and looking at their feet, the turtles or watching the fish swim by and know what the bottom of the creek bed looks like. I have no idea what can be done to clean up the mess we have made over the years. This did not start out to be a piece about "climate change" but up close this is, in my opinion, what climate change looks like. This is about one creek. I think about how much damage is being done to the environment and to the earth we are leaving to future generations. That creek was most likely there hundreds or maybe even thousands of years and was running clear 70 — 75 years ago. After all those years, it was running clear for me to enjoy as a child. That is no longer the case. What a shame.

The creeks ran clear back then. I wonder if children who see this creek today think it was always green and still, and what would Mr. Cook think?

Three Stories from the 1970's

Midtown in the 1970s

It was a different time (1970s) and Wilson was like most Southern (and other parts of the country) towns. Entertainment was mostly segregated. There were a few supper clubs and/or night clubs in town. White folks went to their clubs and Black folks went to theirs. On some occasions the lines were crossed. This story is how I had the experience of going to Midtown which was a black club and at the time I went it was located on Nash Street. It was not much to look at on the outside and I don't know what it looked like in the daytime but when I saw it with the decorations and the lighting and that beautiful colorful lighted dance floor — all I could think was that it was way too fancy for Wilson. It was amazing. It belonged in New York or Las Vegas. Anyway, a friend of mine was invited to Midtown and bring a few guests. Yes, when I was invited, you know I went. I asked a friend of mine who was a real "countrified" guy, and I knew he wouldn't be too comfortable going but I persuaded him to go along with about 5 others. When we arrived, we were met by the owner or manager who went by name of "Smokey." He welcomed us to Midtown and had a table reserved for us right up next to that beautiful lighted dance floor. I don't remember ever being treated so nice and made to feel welcome not only by Smokey but by all who were there. People were dancing and I was thoroughly enjoying watching the moves — some dances I was not familiar with. I was having a great time, but I noticed my country friend was a little uncomfortable. Our table was a long table, and a regular patron of Midtown was sitting at one end of the table — he was the coolest of all, wearing a trench coat, cap and sunglasses. He appeared to be aware of country boy's nervousness. The cool guy says to the country boy "Hey man, everything is alright." Country boy said, "I certainly hope so". The others of us at the table were having a great time and watching the dancing.

Smokey comes over to the table and says we should join in the dancing . One couple got up and danced. Smokey says to me "You are at Midtown and what a shame not to dance." I said "I don't know how to do those dances." He said, "Just come on with me to the floor and do exactly what I say. You will be dancing just like these guys do." That's what I did. He would say, "Two steps to the right. Turn this way." Anyway, it took a few minutes, but it was fun, and I was having a great time. I know I wasn't making all the tight steps, but I felt like I was. I don't know how many people remember Midtown when it was on Nash Street, but I am glad I went and saw firsthand the grace the people in that club had. Oh yeah, I have to say one more thing — I don't know where those girls shopped but they were some classy gorgeous outfits. I know they didn't get them in Wilson. Those outfits and that lighted dance floor had it going on. That was fifty years ago.

I just thought about this and felt like sharing.

It was the Damnedest Party

We were not teenagers. I was about 40 at the time so youth and immaturity are no excuse. In my 86 years I have been to a lot of parties, this is a story about the wildest and craziest party I ever went to. I have partied from Los Angeles, Houston, New Orleans, Miami, Las Vegas, New York City, Wilbanks, Elm City and Pender's Crossroads and places in between. This memorable Party started out as a gathering of a few friends to celebrate Lori's birthday. it was the mid-1970s. I will change the names of the participants, but the account of the party is accurate. The host of the party was a successful businessman I will call Brad — His date Anne, Me and my date I will call Art. An out of town Attorney I will call Fred and his wife Lori. A friend of the host from New York City who I will call Tootsie. He was alone and was slight in build. I remember most everyone else dressed for a party, but Tootsie wore baggy Khaki shorts and sandals. There was a few others there but less than a dozen people, so it was a small group.

Everyone was having a great time — the kind of gathering that everything is funny, and everyone is laughing. Background music is disco — it was the 1970s. Periodically Tootsie would jump onto a chair and dance for a while — He isn't being a show off. It is obvious that he is in his own zone.

The party is well underway, and a few drinks have been consumed. Anne realized that the big Birthday Cake had not been touched and so she grabbed the cake and held it up like a trophy while we all sang Happy Birthday to Lori. Lori made her wish and blew out the single candle. Just as she was backing away from the cake — Ann pushed that big frosted cake into Lori's face cake icing all over her face and in her hair. Lori grabs both hands into the cake and smears cake and icing all over Anne's face and hair, Brad steps in and takes control of the cake and starts throwing cake on everyone and giving them cake to throw. There's sticky icing on everybody and on the ceiling. The cake was almost gone, so Brad goes to the refrigerator and brings out Redi-Whip, butter and squeeze Parkay margarine. Now everyone has ammunition, and the gooey mess is all over everybody's clothes, hair, on the furniture, drapes, walls, floors just everywhere. Brad sees that the Redi Whip may be getting low, so he goes into another room and comes out with an arm full of shaving cream aerosol cans — the kind that squirts out like whipped cream. Now everyone is squirting shaving cream on top of birthday cake, butter, Redi Whip and margarine. Nobody got mad. Everyone is laughing while covered in this gooey mess. Tootsie is standing on his chair swaying to the disco tunes and things are beginning to calm a bit. BUT not yet — Brad grabs a fire extinguisher and holds it like a tommy gun in a gangster movie, shooting the gunk onto the ceilings and the walls, into the lights fixtures, windows. He fired it at Tootsie 's chair and was backing up as he knock on the door and broke the glass. At this exact moment one of the guys who had been invited to the party but didn't come because he had a first date with a beauty queen and socialite heiress. He arrived to introduce his date to a few of his good friends who he told her were nice and he thought she would like them. They entered the door to see the host with his fire extinguisher, Tootsie dancing in his chair and the rest of us covered in the gooey mess and laughing like hyenas.

I have to admire that beauty queen socialite — once the initial look of Horror left her face, she entered the room with the confidence and determination of Scarlett O'Hara and was making offers to try to help get the gook off faces.

WT, the guy who brought her removed her pretty quickly, but I do wonder what she thought of her date's friends. It was the wildest party I ever went to.

I believe the house had to have furniture removed, cleaning crew and a new paint job and a new door. WOW it was quite a party.

It was the 1970s.

Life Is Short.

Believe Me, You Do Not Want to Go Back

Believe me when I tell you that you do not want to "go back."

This is the way it was in the early 1970s.

I had been living in Florida and married with two children. I returned to Wilson, my hometown, as a "separated woman." I was trying to get my life in order. I had a job, found a car and needed a loan to purchase. That was a difficult situation for a separated woman. I was a Sales Representative for a Truck Body Company and worked in the Carolinas and Virginia. I drove a company car for work but needed a personal car. I went to the bank I had worked at years prior, and they did not feel comfortable making a loan to a "separated woman," so I went to First Union Bank and spoke to Robert. I had known him through banking classes in years past. He took the information, and I explained my situation. He said he would need to have my Financial Statement on file. Of course, I didn't have one and I asked him to help me prepare one. He went into another office and came back in a few minutes and said he had it and my loan had been approved. What a relief that was. Then he asked if I had the money for insurance and license. I did not. He added that amount onto the loan. I will never forget his kindness. Now, I just had to get auto insurance. I left and went to the bank I had worked some years prior because they had an Insurance Department and I had been pretty good friends with the Manager of the Insurance Department. He was nice and friendly and "great to see you." etc. BUT he said he could not write my auto insurance because I was a "separated woman" and considered a bad risk. So, from there I went to several agencies and was given the same reason they could not insure me. Finally, I went to State Farm (this is not a plug for them). The agent at that agency was new to the business and I guess he was willing to take a risk, so he wrote my insurance.

As my children got older and we purchased a car for my son, State Farm insured it. Then my daughter got a car and they insured hers. Then I bought a house, and they wrote a Homeowners Policy on my house. All is going great, and I did put in a plug for that agency when I could.

About fifteen years passed and I had worked out of state for a while for a Motivational Company and returned to Wilson. I took a job as manager of a hotel. I was in the lobby one evening when the manager of the insurance department at the bank I had worked for in the 1950s when the guy who had refused to write my auto insurance because I was a poor risk came in for a Rotary Meeting. He had an out of town guest with him. He stopped at the lobby desk and spoke, and I was polite and spoke to him. The conversation went kind of like this:

Him: He looked at his male guest and then at me and said "Ain't she purty?" I did not like it, but I let it slide.

Him: "One thing about it though, she does not buy her insurance from me." Again, I smiled and let it slide. Then he said directly to me.

"Why don't you buy your insurance from me?"

Me: Emmitt, you really don't want to know."

Him: "Yes I do."

Me: "I don't think you do."

Him: "Yes, I do."

Me: In my best Julia Sugarbaker style: "OK, I will tell you. I came back to Wilson in the early 70s and went to you and asked you to write my auto insurance and you told me that you could not because 'I was a poor risk as a separated woman." I did get insurance from your competitor. NOW I have had that insurance with his agency for fifteen years and now have THREE cars that are paid for and insured. I have bought a house and put in a swimming pool and that agency also insures my house. I have not filed ANY claims so "poor risk" that I was then I think I have been a pretty safe risk. I know all this was because I was a separated woman. Let me say this to you — "Poor risk that I was my three cars are paid for and my house now has a pool, and the best part is that I have done all this as a separated woman without attaching myself to any son of a bitchin' man."

This insurance guy couldn't get out fast enough. His guest who he was trying to impress laughed and reached over the counter and said to me. "Good for you and I am so happy to meet you." About this same time, it was just as difficult for a separated woman to get a credit card. I navigated through all this bull just like many other women. Trust me, it is not an easy thing especially when there are children to support. The only reason I am posting this is because of what the Supreme Court is doing. Women, please protest. Please call your representatives. Do whatever you can. You do not want to go back. There are many ways they can take us back to "Handmaid's Tale." When I first started working, an employer who was interviewing a female could legally ask (and they did) if you were pregnant and/or if you planned to get pregnant. In some cases, if a female employee got pregnant, she was fired when she started "showing." That was not the image they wanted. No, no, we do not want to go back there. I didn't think it could happen in today's world. I now know that it can and IS.

William Greene, early 1930's

Collection of Writings
by William T. Greene

I just had to include these writings by my father. His stories are warm and informative. He told us so many things and I wish he had put them in writing. He was busy living his long and happy life of 101 years (1909- 2010).

His story about Aunt Cindy is one of many that he told, and it was transcribed from his verbal conversation. The story about Jake and Greta is one we have heard for many years. He actually wrote this one by hand himself before losing his eyesight. The Si Whitley story is one that has been pretty well documented in newspaper articles from the time it happened in the late 1880s and is part of the neighborhood history and legend. My dad's story is in his own words. He talked with some of the people involved. My great grandfather Wiggins, who passed away in 1959, was in the buggy with Dr. Barnes when they came upon the victims.

His poem "Hunter's Moon" is one of my favorites. The story he wrote about how he came to write the poem is just priceless. The details in his story bring life to the time and place.

His story related by Cousin Pat is a family favorite and I am happy it is included.

He was a great talent both in his paintings and writing. I believe he would want folks to read and enjoy a few of his stories.

Jake and Greta "Memories Worth Keeping"

By William Greene

"This is a story about two English Setter puppies, Jake and Greta. Jake was 12 months old, and Greta was 4 months old. Jake had been hunted some and grew up to be one of two of the best quail dogs I ever saw. Greta was a puppy that tried to please, and I always started training them as soon as they could get out of their bed to retrieve a dummy made out of an RJR smoking tobacco bag that had been washed to get the tobacco smell out. I would fill the bag with quail feathers or maybe a foot or a wing. Greta loved to play "hide and seek" with this dummy. Let someone hide it and take her nearby and say "dead bird" and she would put her nose up in the air and go to smelling the wind. She would always find it and come running to you so pleased acting. All this happened in 1933. (Writing this in 2003 so that was about 70 years ago) but I remember it as if it was today.

This is the part and the main reason I am writing this story.

One evening I took Jake and Greta out for a short time. I knew where I could usually find several coveys very easily. I just wanted to find one. There was a cornfield with a hedgerow and a ditch on each side, a branch nearby. As soon as we got in the cornfield, grass shoe top high, both puppies could smell birds. They both could almost point and move on, and they both pointed at the end of the field. I flushed them and killed one. He fell nearest to Greta. Both puppies saw him fall and both puppies went after him. Jake took the bird away from Greta and brought him on. The singles lighted in a place that the branch had overflowed and still about half the ground was covered with water. Leaves had rafted up among the few trees and some water was about 3 or 4 inches deep. Jake was off to my left and Greta was about ten steps to my right. I stepped near enough to flush a bird and killed him. Greta saw the bird and hurried to him and was bringing him to me when she saw Jake coming. She was standing in about 3 or 4 inches of water. She stopped and put the quail under the water and put her foot on him. She dropped her tail and looked around as if she was interested in nothing at all. Jake went on by and she quickly picked the bird up from underneath the water and hurried on to me so happy. I don't know whether dogs laugh or not. I do believe Greta was smiling and trying to say 'we put one over on Jake that time, didn't we.' That's the conversation we had anyway.

Greta, I remember, retrieved one more bird. I took Greta and her mother down to where some men were cutting wood for me. The old dog pointed near an old colored graveyard about 20 steps away. I walked over and flushed them and killed one. He fell in an old blown down tree with long limbs with vines and briars grown up in it. The woodcutter said 'you won't ever find that bird.' The old dog went around the opposite side and Greta went in next to where I was standing. There was a clear place in there and Greta went in, and the bird had fell through all the vines and she picked him up and came out so pleased as usual.

At the age of six months Greta had distemper and died. I never named another dog Greta. That name belonged to a little English Setter puppy I would like to have with me anywhere.

Well, I have to stop now. I got something in my eye.

Cousin Pat

A Story Told by William Greene

William Greene was asked to contribute a story about family history for a book on *History of Wilson County.* This is the story he told in 1985:

I KNOW HISTORY IS BIASED; the losers never get to write it. One side is always glorified. The Romans always fought the barbarians, whoever they were. I would like to repeat a little bit of Legend as I heard it many years ago. Legend is more truth than written History.

Cousin Pat was my grandfather's cousin. She was interested in saving seeds from all kinds of plants and just as interested in her for-bearers. She said the first Wiggins to come here was Noah Wiggins, her great grandfather. He was with the Colonial Army and his feet got frostbitten so that he could not walk to keep up with his company and was put out by the roadside about where Emporia, Va. is now. A widow woman who lived nearby took him in and kept him until his feet were well enough to rejoin his regiment.

After the War he went back and married the widow and moved to the turpentine woods where she then lived, what is now Wilson County (then Edgecombe County). They farmed and sold tar, pitch and turpentine at Old Sparta.

They were neighbors and friends with the Shallingtons, who owned a lot of land, a gristmill and a store. The big earthen dam is still standing except for where it was cut in the middle to drain the pond during the Civil War. Bill Shallington owned a Negro boy called Trustyboy Hector. He sent him up into the loft of the store to get some horseshoes with a "litard torch" (lightwood torch) to light the way and he exploded a keg of gunpowder that blew the top off the store. The top and Trustyboy ended up in about twelve inches of water in the millpond about on hundred and ten steps away. He lost a leg at the hip but lived to be an old man.

The Shallingtons and Wiggins hunted and fished together. Cousin Pat said her favorite place to catch redfins (duckbilled pike) was the Fort Hole. All the deepest places on Town Creek had names. The Fort Hole was named for a tribe of Indians that lived there. The Fort Field is on the South side of Town Creek and on the North Side of the Sheriff William D. Petway farm is a flat topped rock about twelve inches above the ground and about sixteen feet square that the Indians must have sat on while making arrowheads.

You could pick up buckets full of flint chips around this rock and the area near it is the best place I ever knew to find arrowheads. This rock is covered now since tractors and heavy machinery have worked the topsoil to it. It was visible in the 1940s and 1950s. There were also two white rocks in the woods nearby as big as a Cadillac car. I am sure they are still there. They are the only ones I ever knew in this region above ground. Aunt Pat said the Indians had a fort there, at least that is what she was told. She did not know when they left or why. They probably left with the Tuscarora when they went North. (Signed by William Greene)

The Charles Henry Wiggins Family

Almon Wiggins was born near Town Creek. He married Catherine Carter, daughter of John Carter who lived in the Gardners School area on what is now known as the Mark Lee Ellis Home Place.

Almon and Catherine bought the farm across from Gardners School. He operated a store on the spot the Gardners School Gym now stands facing the Saratoga Road. There was an oak tree on each side of the front of the store. One tree is still standing. (Signed by William Greene)

A Little More About Grandma's Lye Soap

(William Greene)

I WOULD LIKE TO TELL just a little more about Grandma's lye soap. Only one person could stir it. It would not make soap if more than one person stirred it. I learned later that she was just trying to keep us children away from near the fire. She would test the soap as it was cooking by taking a chicken wing feather and dipping it in the hot soap and if it ate the web off, it was strong enough.

She would take a soap paddle and dip up some and if it would rope like honey, it was cooked enough.

If you made soap on the shrinking of the moon it would shrink and if you made it on the growing of the moon it would not

Also, next to the Old Barn there were twenty-five ancient Mulberry trees with fruit as long and as big as your finger. They kept the hogs fat in May with a little corn in the evenings to keep the mulberries from edging the hog's teeth — so Grandpa said.

Two of the trees had white berries that were sickening sweet. We never ate them but when our friends came on the weekends to play ball, they sat up in the Mulberry trees most of the time.

So not even an artist could paint all of this on one canvas, so I wrote a poem on the bottom part of the canvas since the Hunter's Moon was shining as bright as day almost and a good time to go fox hunting. Here's the poem:

Why I Wrote Poem – "The Hunter's Moon"

I WANTED TO PAINT A picture of the old barn and of fond memories of the way it was. In retrospect I painted the old barn, but I could not paint a picture of a half circle of a row of corn in the shucks around the barn door. The whole bottom of the canvas was empty.

I wanted to include the mule stables, the cow stable, the big stove wood pile cone shaped, the wash pots my grandma made her lye soap in, the fox hounds lying around anxious to go after a fox, for it was September and The Hunter's Moon was as big as a wagon wheel just over the tree tops in the East. And in retrospect my grandfather in the front yard sitting in a chair with his friends talking of hound dogs as they drift to the Old Barn for a "Full Blush of the Goblet of Nash County's Best."

And the stories they could tell on each other. Of course, I could not paint a picture of all this, so I started to write on the bottom of the canvas as follows.

The Hunter's Moon
(William Greene)

The plows and wagons
are under the shelter.
The disc and stalk-cutter
are out of the weather.
The hoes and shovels
Are staked away.
The loft is full of pea-vine hay.
The barn is full of corn in the ear.
And that's my neighbor's
hunting horn I hear.
The persimmons are ripe
and extra good fare.
The fox is strong
with a new coat of hair.
He thinks he can outsmart
any pack that treats him fair.
And if Old Rock keeps
cutting on him, he'll hang
him on a wire fence
he knows just where.
The pack is in danger
of ketchin' after
a six-hour chase.

With a turkey mouth yelp,
a chop and a bawl,
And you can identify them all,
he hurries to his
blown-down den twenty feet tall.
They didn't "ketch" but he
deserves the dead blow
of three long blasts
from the hunter's horn
for a chase under
The Hunter's Moon

The Story of Si Whitley

(as told by William Greene and transcribed)

SI WHITLEY LIVED ON HWY 42 on what is now known as the Cozart Farm. People don't know exactly where Si came from. It is told that he was a Yankee deserter. He lived somewhere around Little Washington, NC, when he and his wife came to Wilson County around 1864 or 1865.

Si loved women with long hair and over a period of time he picked up seven wives in the neighborhood. It is told if he saw a woman he wanted, he would simply take her. The women were scared to cross him in any way and if one would make him mad, he would nearly beat her to death.

If Si saw something in the neighborhood he wanted, he would take it. He was a terror, and everyone hated him. There were only a couple of people that he respected. They were Hilliard Williams and Martha Forbes. Martha had a cow to get gone one night and Si told her not to worry that her cow would be returned. The next day two black men returned the cow. For some reason he was afraid of Hilliard Williams, and he liked Joe and Martha Forbes.

He got into several fights with people for virtually no reason. On the day before he was ambushed, he and xxxxxxxxx had a fight at Bridgersville, which is located on Hwy 42. Si also seemed to have power with the local law as he could steal, rob, and fight but the law turned its head. As there was no law and order in the South at that period after the Civil War, he seemed to have connections with the law in Wilson.

Early one morning in 1890 Tom Wiggins and Dr. Ben Barnes were going to the first tobacco auction in their buggy to Wilson. They came upon Si Whitley lying in the road which is now Hwy 42. Tom

Wiggins picked his head up and he was bleeding. Dr. Barnes told him to put him back down. They rode about a half a mile down the road and saw a buggy turned in at a farm house. They found Robert Whitley across a tub of barbecue. He was dead.

It has been told through generations that five men were sitting in ambush and shot Si and Robert. These were four white men and one black man. Xxxxxxx loaded the guns and one gun was loaded with blanks. It is said that xxxxxxxx was one of the white men and xxxxxxxxx was the black man. Over the years the other names that were rumored have been forgotten.

They had a big dance and party at Si Whitley's house that night. Mr. Ed Pender said someone should go to help Si's wives shroud the bodies. I would not say it was the same barbecue that Robert died in, but barbecue was on the table according to Mr. Ed Pender.

One of Si's women told this story.

If she didn't have 200 lbs. of cotton picked that day, he would beat her. She had a sick baby and knew she couldn't get it done. Si got killed that day and the lady remarked that was one whipping she wouldn't get. It is rumored that there was eight women and fifty-two children living in that house.

It was told that after Si's and Robert's deaths the women and children partied because they were glad they were gone.

(Story told by William Greene)

*Author's Note: I have read stories reported in the newspaper Wilson Advance, dated March 8, 1888, and April 17, 1890. The stories are almost identical to the way William Greene remembers it being told by his grandfather, Dr. Barnes and Ed Pender. William Greene was not born until 1909 so his information is directly from people who were knowledgeable about the incident. The newspaper articles are very detailed and give more information about the activities, skirmishes and lockups of Si Whitley.

Names of some of the men who were rumored to have been part of the ambush have been exed out in William Greene's story. I was unable to find any names in newspaper articles of the men who were rumored to have been involved in the ambush. The articles I read reported the ambush as "unsolved." The Wilson County Public Library archives has many newspaper articles and record of Court proceedings that provide more details on this legendary case. It has been 132 years since the death of Si Whitley, but it has been talked about and referred to for generations around the Crossroads and beyond.

Message to Aunt Cindy

(This story was transcribed from my father's own words: His message to his Aunt Cindy: Transcribed from his own words when he was 96 years old)

AUNT CINDY, I KNOW IT was very tedious work for you to pick all that cotton, pick out the seeds and card it into bats. At your quilting parties, I wonder if it would be the same conversations, you would have today. At grandma's quilting parties there was one old lady who didn't quilt but just smoked her pipe. They'd talk about everything, even about married couples that had their first baby and if the baby had time to get here.

Aunt Cindy, I know if you throw a stone into a pond, it makes waves. These waves never end, and they go on until they hit a bank but still make waves. I think I have heard that sound waves are the same way — they never cease but just get weaker. It is very common that you can hear an echo. If they ever made something like a graphophone, I would like to have one so I could select what sound waves I want to hear and block out the ones I don't want to hear.

I am sure that most of the women dipped snuff. Most of them used the bottom of a beggar weed bush. They chewed it into a mop at one end and put it into the snuff tin to dip out the snuff. The men folks put the snuff in their lip. I never saw but one man that sniffed it up his nose. They always had a spittoon underneath the quilting table and if there was a crawling baby on the floor make sure he didn't get into the spittoon. Of all the things you had to carry out, the spittoon was the worst. I remember my grandma carrying it out to the wash pot that had a long handle gourd dipper. She would take water from the gourd dipper and wash out the spittoon.

There was one lady at the quilting party that took long stitches and she thought she was doing as good as anybody. At night grandma would take her stitches out and short stitch it. They did this without her knowing about it.

My great grandma Martha Forbes was a hardworking lady. Her husband was disabled when he came home from the Civil War. In her garden she raised all kinds of herbs and spices. She was well known for her seed corn. She went to the fields and selected her seed corn. She wanted an ear that grew middle way the stalk and short arm hanging down. She was famous for her seed corn and was advertised in a magazine many years ago. Yes, I would like to hear Grandma on the phone telling how she planted her corn and how she fed her livestock to keep them so fine looking. I remember her corn had a red ear in it once in a while. The Indians knew the food value of different corns. There should never be white and yellow corn on the same cob. Blue corn and white or any other color is ok. Different colors had different vitamins and food value. The first meal a sow got after she found pigs was two or three ears of red corn.

I remember when I was about 18 months old my grand dad took me down to see the pigs. He told me to pick up two ears of red corn to give to them. I remember seeing that big bed of pigs and asking where did the sow find them. Pa would tell me she found them in a stump hole. That would be the same stump hole Lucy found her puppies.

About three years later, I forgot that Chester was a colored boy who used to pull me in his little red wagon. He wanted to be a horse that ran away and turned me over and that was so funny to him. One day we were looking at a stump hole that was full of water where a tree had blown over last year. I said to Chester, "Let's see if there are any pigs in this stump hole." We went wading around in that hole looking for pigs when an old bullfrog jumped out. We didn't say a word. We just left them where they were.

Aunt Cindy's Featherbed:

Aunt Cindy was a prominent name for many generations. Every newlywed had a featherbed. It finally came my time, and we took a featherbed to use for a while. Aunt Cindy and Uncle Hansel were probably born around 1800, a couple of years either way. I was one of the last ones to get a featherbed handed down by my Aunt Cindy. We used it for a while and then put it away. I expect that featherbed was about 200 years old when one day my wife, Dell, was cleaning. She had someone helping her who asked if she could have that featherbed. Dell gave it to her. From my house it looked like a big snow. One thing we do know is that they did have white geese 200 years ago. Aunt Cindy, we will keep your quilt. I know several people who have one of her quilts she was famous for.

Aunt Cindy, we had a pretty quilt of yours with a paisley pattern. The top was paisley — looked like a tadpole or crooked necked squash — always hard to tell. We will give it to several generations. The quilt was threadbare. A lady wanted to fix it but, Aunt Cindy, your quilt top was put away for safekeeping. You take the seeds out of the cotton, then card the cotton and then lay it right thick and quilt it together as thick as you want it. At the quilting, it seems most of the women dipped snuff — the snuff brush was beggar weed root. You had to watch the children to keep them out of the spittoons. Beggar weed root was last found where Jim planted pine trees.

A Gift from My Father

IT WAS THE FALL OF 1940 and on this particular night there was a full moon. It appeared to be so close you could reach out and touch it.

My father had walked outside and, of course, I followed him. He started telling me about the moon and the stars. I was between three and four years old, so I did not understand much of his explanation except that I was highly attracted to the moon and I still am. As we walked around the yard on that moonlit night, I asked my dad to "get the moon for me." He explained that He couldn't reach it. I did not accept that.

There was a clothes line in the back yard. A weeding hoe leaned against the clothes line pole and I told my dad that if he would take the hoe, he could jump up and reach the moon and get it for me.

He took the weeding hoe and started trying to reach that full moon. He reached as high as he could, and it just didn't happen. He even jumped a few times.

He squatted and took me on his knee. He said, "I cannot get it down, but it is yours. I give it to you. We have to leave it where it is, but it will always be yours."

That was 82 years ago, and I still claim the moon as mine. Whenever I am with people and someone says something about the moon being so beautiful, I just cannot help myself, I always say, "Yes, it is, and it belongs to me. My father gave it to ME. You can look at it and enjoy it. You can even claim it for yourself. You just have to claim it like I have." This conversation must have happened hundreds of times over these 82 years.

What a gift.

Ingram Content Group UK Ltd.
Milton Keynes UK
UKHW011551060323
418095UK00012B/1483